Spring Miscellany
and London Essays

Sōseki Natsume (1867–1916) is widely considered the foremost novelist of the Meiji period (1868–1914). After graduating from Tokyo Imperial University in 1893, Sōseki taught high school before spending two years in England on a Japanese government scholarship. He returned to lecture in English literature at the university. Numerous nervous disorders forced him to give up teaching in 1908 and he became a full-time writer for the *Asahi* newspaper. In addition to fourteen novels, Sōseki wrote haiku, poems in the Chinese style, academic papers on literary theory, essays, autobiographical sketches and fairy tales.

Sammy I. Tsunematsu is founder and curator of the Sōseki Museum in London, and the translator of several of Sōseki's works. He has also researched and published widely on the Japanese artist Yoshio Markino, who was a contemporary of Sōseki's living in London at the beginning of the twentieth century. Tsunematsu has lived in Surrey, England, for nearly thirty years.

Sōseki Natsume

Spring Miscellany
and London Essays

Translated and Introduced by
Sammy I. Tsunematsu

TUTTLE PUBLISHING
Boston • Rutland, Vermont • Tokyo

Published by Tuttle Publishing
an imprint of Periplus Editions (HK) Ltd,
with editorial offices at 153 Milk Street, Boston, Massachusetts, 01209 and
130 Joo Seng Road, #06-01/03, Singapore 368357.

Originally published in Japanese as *Eijitsu Shōhin*, 1909
English translation © Sammy I. Tsunematsu, 2002
First Tuttle edition, 2002

Library of Congress Cataloging Card No. 2002102260
ISBN 0 8048 3326 5

The Translator would like to acknowledge the assistance of
John Edmondson who kindly read through the English version
and made many helpful changes.

Printed in Singapore

Distributed by:

North America, Latin America & Europe
Tuttle Publishing
Airport Industrial Park, 464 Innovation Drive
North Clarendon, VT 05759-9436
Tel: (802) 773 8930; Fax: (802) 773 6993

Japan & Korea
Tuttle Publishing
Yaekari Building, 3F, 5-4-12 Osaki
Shinagawa-ku, Tokyo 153 0064
Tel: (03) 5437 0171; Fax: (03) 5437 0755

Asia Pacific
Berkeley Books Pte Ltd
130 Joo Seng Road, #06-01/03 Singapore 368357
Tel: (65) 2680 1330; Fax: (65) 2680 6290

Contents

Introduction

Sōseki Natsume (1867–1916) is regarded as one of Japan's greatest writers. In 1984, he became the first literary celebrity to grace a Japanese banknote when his portrait appeared on the new 1000 yen note. His novels continue to be popular, and attract a wide readership among both children and adults.

For a short period at the beginning of the twentieth century, from 1900 to 1902, Sōseki lived in London. The recent centenary of his stay in London was marked by various commemorative events, including a lecture by his granddaughter, Yōko Matsuoka McClain ("Sōseki: A Granddaughter's View"). On 22 March 2002, a "blue plaque" was unveiled at 81 The Chase, in South London, the writer's last London home. Sōseki was the first Japanese person to be honored in this way, joining the company of other English luminaries such as Charles Dickens, (Sir Arthur) Conan Doyle and John Lennon.

However, Sōseki's two-year stay in London was dismal and solitary. His memories of the experience are described in a famous passage in his Preface to *The Criticism of Literature* (*Bungakuron*):

The two years I spent in London were the most unpleasant years in my life. Among English gentlemen I lived in misery, like a poor dog that had strayed among a pack of wolves.

When Sōseki wrote *Spring Miscellany*, he was forty-three years old. His major works had already been published—*I am a Cat* (1905), *Botchan* (1906), *The Three-Cornered World* (1906), *Wild Poppies* (1907) and *Sanshiro* (1908)—and he was firmly established as a major novelist. *Spring Miscellany*, a collection of short essays, demonstrates Sōseki's ability as a short story writer. In this volume, I have also included the first translations of "The Carlyle Museum" and "The Diary of a Bicycle Rider", as well as some of Sōseki's letters from London, to help towards a better understanding of the author's stay in the city.

Spring Miscellany comprises eight short stories and seventeen essays, eight of which are recollections of Sōseki's time in London. These pieces first appeared in the Tokyo and Osaka editions of the *Asahi* newspaper, between 14 January and 9 March 1909. Some of the essays closely resemble chapters in his book *Ten Nights' Dreams* (1908); for example, the story of the strange experience in "The Snake" reminds us of the "Fourth Night" while "The Heart" is similar to the "Tenth Night".

The stories "The Persimmon" and "The Human Being" illustrate the gulf between wealth and poverty. "Mona Lisa" concerns a man with no knowledge of art and no interest in it. "The Kakemono" and "The Voice" portray the everyday lives of ordinary people. Taken as a whole, the collection focuses on the uneducated lower middle-class worker. Sōseki is one of the very few Japanese writers to have tackled the subject of money—traditionally considered an inappropriate subject for literature in Japan. The Pheasant" in this collection is similar to *I am a Cat*.

The essay "New Year's Day" records the day Sōseki spent with the *haiku*[1] poet Takahama Kyoshi.

---

[1] A short 17-syllable verse form consisting of three metrical units of five, seven and five syllables respectively.

"The Thief" describes a true incident. "The Pheasant" concerns a young student who wants to be a writer and who visits the *Mokuyō-kai* ("Thursday Group") held at Sōseki's house. "The Cat's Grave" recalls Sōseki's description of the death of his dog in *Inside My Glass Doors* (2002).

As we have already noted, this collection includes eight pieces based on Sōseki's residence in England. "The Boarding House" and "Odor of the Past" recall his first lodging house, at 85 Priory Road, West Hampstead in North West London. In "The Boarding House", Sōseki writes:

That evening a bald, elderly man with a white beard took his place at the dinner table. After the spinster had informed me that he was her father, I noticed that my host was an old man. He had a curious way of expressing himself. It was immediately obvious that he was not English. I gathered that father and daughter had crossed the Channel to settle in England. Then, as if purposely anticipating my enquiry, he told me he was German.... His daughter's severe visage seemed to become still more so when she spoke to her father. I was completely unable to believe that their relations were normal. Such were the thoughts that filled my mind that night when I went to sleep.

All the people whom Sōseki describes in "The Boarding House" are modelled on people he actually met. For example, the original of the elderly man described in the above extract was a Prussian named Frederick Milde, the proprietor of the two branches of F. Milde & Son, "Military Tailors and Outfitters", located at 5 Conduit Street and 3 George Street in the West End of London. Milde was 69 years old when Sōseki knew him. He lived with Mariya Muller (51 years old), whom Sōseki assumed to be his wife,

Antonia Doring (36), German national Voltaire Paot (20) and housemaid Agnes Brice (15).

According to the Census of 1901, released on 2 January 2002, seven people were living at 6 Flodden Road, Camberwell, in South West London. These included K. Natsume, whose occupation was listed as "Instructor of Literature". It has been thought that the landlord, a Mr Brett, was a doctor of engineering, but according to the Census his occupation was General Buyer for Furies and he was only 25 years old. His wife Sarah was 40, fifteen years older. Her sister Catherine Sparrow (36) helped with domestic work. Isabel Roberts (18), who played table tennis with Sōseki, was a student. Finally, there were Tanaka Kōtaro, a 27-year-old Japanese businessman, and Annie Penn, a 23-year-old domestic servant.

Sōseki's last home in London—81 The Chase, Clapham Common, London SW4—was his favorite. He found it by placing an advertisement in *The Daily Telegraph* on 11 July 1901:

Board Residence wanted, by a Japanese gentleman, in a strictly private English family, with literary taste. Quiet and convenient quarters in N., N.W., or S.W. preferred—Address, Z. V., care of Barker, 2, Castle-court, Birchin-lane, E.C.

He stayed there for one year and five months. The landlady was Priscilla Leale, 58 years old, born in Frome, Somerset. She ran the boarding house with her sister Elizabeth (48), who had lived for a time in the Channel Islands. Sōseki must have been referring to Elizabeth when he wrote that the landlady even spoke French and had a good knowledge of William Shakespeare and John Milton. Sōseki did not know that French was widely spoken in the Channel Islands. I have been privileged to obtain a rare photograph of Priscilla and Elizabeth from one of their descendants, which is reproduced here.

"In this house, two old ladies and a retired officer live," Sōseki wrote to Masaoka Shiki on 10 February 1902. The retired officer was 79-year-old Anstell Melsh, who had been a colonel in the army. It was during his stay in this lodging house that Sōseki suffered from deep depression. Priscilla and Elizabeth were very concerned about him, as he seldom emerged from his room and spent most of the day reading. They suggested to him that he should take up bicycle riding for exercise (bicycle riding was a very popular pastime in Britain at the beginning of the twentieth century). Out of his experiences with the bicycle, Sōseki produced his comic short story "The Diary of a Bicycle Rider".

Around the beginning of October 1902, Sōseki was invited to Pitlochry in Scotland by the ex-solicitor and art collector John Henry Dixon (born 3 June 1838 at Wakefield, Yorkshire; died 20 October 1926 at Clachnafaire in Scotland), who had an avid interest in Japanese art and culture. In his essay "In Bygone Days", Sōseki describes his impressions:

The Valley of Pitlochry belongs to the days of a hundred or two hundred years ago and settles down without resistance under a patina of dullness. The faces bronzed by autumn turn towards the sky and contemplate the clouds passing above the mountains. These clouds are at once white, then gray. Through their transparent background one can frequently see the hillsides, no matter at what moment one looks at them. These clouds seem as if they have always been there.

The house that welcomed me was at the top of a hill and provided a good viewing point for the clouds and the valley. It faced south and the sun bathed every part of its walls.

The visit to Pitlochry must have been a wonderful holiday for Sōseki. It is unclear how he met John Dixon, but it may have been through the Japan Society, of which Dixon was a member. Dixon had brought over gardeners from Japan and had constructed a beautiful model of Mount Fuji in his garden. He was also a great collector of watercolors by Japanese artists, including Markino Yoshio, Ioki Bunsai and Ōshita Tōjiro, among others. On 10 December 1902, just after Sōseki had left London, Dixon gave a talk at the Japan Society entitled "On Some Japanese Artists of Today". Undoubtedly, if Sōseki had visited Pitlochry just after his arrival in London instead of towards the end of his stay, his impressions of Britain might have been very different. Sōseki was amazed by the modernity of the country and depressed by the despair. Had he not lived in England, however, we might not have been able to enjoy his novels.

SAMMY I. TSUNEMATSU
Founder/Curator
Soseki Museum in London
July 2002

1
New Year's Day[2]

After consuming a bowl of *zōni*,[3] I retired to my study. Shortly afterwards three or four visitors arrived, all of them young. One of them was wearing a frock coat. It was probably not his everyday clothing, as his movements were awkward, giving the impression that he was at pains to handle the soft fabric with due care. His companions were in Japanese attire, as usual, making not the slightest concession to the New Year. The general surprise thus caused was evident from the "oh's" and "aah's" uttered by everybody on seeing the frock coat. They ended with my own "oh!" of surprise and admiration.

The wearer of the frock coat took out a white handkerchief and wiped his face, without any obvious need to do so. He then drank several glasses of liqueur, one after another, while his companions did not remain inactive but busied themselves with their chopsticks around the little tables provided for them. At this moment, Kyoshi,[4] in turn, arrived in a carriage. He was attired in traditional ceremonial fashion, with a black *haori*[5] and a black kimono bearing his family's coat of arms, as everybody fully expected. I had little doubt that the need to be thus clad was because he practised *nō*, but I asked him

[2] The date is January 1st 1908.
[3] A kind of clear soup seasoned with soya sauce and containing various other ingredients, such as breast of chicken, fish paste, crushed rice grilled in advance and chervil. *Zōni* is part of the traditional New Year menu.
[4] Takahama Kyoshi (1874–1959), a poet and a friend of Sōseki who edited the literary journal *Hohotogisu*.
[5] A jacket put on over a kimono.

nevertheless. "Yes," he replied, "That's true." He then suggested singing a *nō*. I said that I saw no objection.

We then recited, all together, a piece entitled "Tōboku".[6] It was a long time since I had learnt this piece and I had practically never worked on it, so that I was, to say the least, unsure about certain passages. Furthermore, my voice sounded stranger than I had expected. When I had finished, the comments came thick and fast. The young people among our listeners declared unanimously, as if they had agreed on this among themselves in advance, that I had been undeniably bad. The wearer of the frock coat declared that I had a quivering voice. None of them knew the slightest thing about *nō* recitations, and I was fully aware that they could not be expected to appreciate Kyoshi's qualities to the full or to form a correct judgment of my own defects. Now that I was their target, however, I had to admit that whether or not they were mere amateurs there were certain grounds for their criticisms. I summoned up the courage to tell them where to get off.

Kyoshi then told us that he had recently started to play the tambourine. The very people who were ignorant of the most elementary rudiments of the art of reciting *no* then vied with one another in urging him to demonstrate his talent. "I'm quite willing, but ..." began Kyoshi, turning to me and asking me to sing the words. Having no idea of the art of accompaniment, I hesitated, but at the same time my curiosity was aroused by the novelty. "All right—I'll sing," I replied. Kyoshi sent for the instrument to be brought by rickshaw. After it had been delivered, I asked for a little stove to be sent to me from the

---

[6] A *nō* libretto, generally attributed to Zeami (1363–1443).

kitchen, and the heat of the embers was allowed to act on the skin of the tambourine. Everybody watched Kyoshi's operations with curiosity. As for me, it was the way in which the instrument was exposed to the fire that caused me some astonishment. I anxiously asked Kyoshi whether the operation would proceed as required. Replying in the affirmative, he tapped the stretched skin of the instrument. The sound was reasonably good. Stating that this was sufficient, Kyoshi removed the stove and set to work to tighten the cords. In his black kimono, bearing the coat of arms, his fingers manipulating the red knots, he exuded a refined elegance for which I was unable to find any extra explanation. This time, admiration was reflected in the glances of all those present.

Shortly afterwards Kyoshi discarded his *haori*. He then picked up the tambourine. I asked him to wait for a moment or two before he started his performance, as I had not the slightest idea of the moment when he intended to strike his instrument and there were certain details that I wished to clear up. Kyoshi carefully explained to me that at a certain moment he would call out in order to accentuate the rhythm, after which he would strike his tambourine in a particular way and all I would then have to do would be to start singing. I found it difficult to follow his explanations. However, if I had waited until I had understood everything, it would have taken us two or three hours. So I reluctantly said that I was ready. I intoned the main piece from "Hagoromo".[7] When I had reached the middle of the verse beginning "The Springtime mists have risen ...", I noticed that my

---

[7] "The Feather Robe", a *no* play attributed to Zeami.

voice lacked the required intensity and regretted that I had agreed to perform. Was my singing not certain to be reduced to a murmur? At the same time, I realized that if I suddenly started to force my voice in the middle of the passage the entire balance of the performance would be destroyed, and I continued by following the indications of the libretto, which, to say the least, were somewhat vague. It was then that Kyoshi gave a shout and administered a hard blow to the tambourine.

I was not expecting Kyoshi to attack the piece with such vigor. I was all the more surprised since I had thought the cries which in the *nō* served to emphasize the rhythm were emitted in a pleasant full voice, but he set my eardrums vibrating and almost gave the impression that his very life was threatened. Taking the rough with the smooth, my recital was two or three times in accordance with the rhythm corresponding to the accompanying cry. Finally, at the moment when the intensity of the voice was decreasing, Kyoshi once again emitted a kind of bellow, which took me by surprise. Every time his voice coincided with my own, mine became more and more hesitant, and was finally imperceptible. The listeners were soon beginning to smother their laughter. Deep down inside me I found the scene more and more absurd. The owner of the frock coat then rose to his feet and burst out laughing. Carried away, I started to laugh in my turn.

I then had to run the gauntlet of my guests' criticisms. The frock coat wearer stood out among them in his intense irony. With a faint smile on his lips, Kyoshi had to sing the text himself, to the accompaniment of his own tambourine, in which he gave a highly successful performance. A little while later, he took his departure in the carriage that was awaiting him, saying that he had further visits to pay. After he had left, the young people continued to subject me to their gibes. Even my wife joined in and, after disparaging her own husband, praised Kyoshi by saying, "When Mr Takahama struck his tambourine, the sleeves of his under-kimono fluttered about, and they had a very nice color!"

"Frock coat" expressed immediate agreement. As for me, both the shade of Kyoshi's kimono sleeves and the undulations they performed left me completely cold.

2
The Snake

When I came out of the garden through the little wooden door on the street, the rain had filled up the deep holes made by a horse's hooves. The sound of the squelching mud under the soles of my feet at every step had a kind of sadness. I held a pail in my right hand, which did not exactly make my progress easier. In order to place one foot in front of the other, I had to find the required rhythm by stretching upwards, and I wished I could get rid of the pail. In the end, the bottom of the pail sank into the mud. At the moment when I was really in danger of losing my balance by bending down to grasp the handle of the pail, I saw my uncle two meters away. His shoulders were covered by a straw cape and he was carrying a big landing net on his back. At the same moment, there was a slight movement of the rush hat protecting his head, and I seemed to hear, from underneath that enormous hat, the words "An abominable road!" Soon afterwards the silhouette enveloped in the straw cape was sodden with rain.

Up on the stone bridge, I leaned over the dark water threading its way between the grasses. It is usually a pretty watercourse of no great depth, reaching to hardly three inches above one's ankles, and one is never tired of gazing at it and the slowly waving grasses, but today the bed of the stream is turbid. Mud spurts forth from it, the rain falling between the clouds thereby formed, and the spiral streams lap over one another and cut through the middle of the river bed. My uncle, after spending a

moment closely observing the swirl, murmurs
"There'll be good fishing!"

Having crossed the bridge, we immediately turn
to the left. The twists and turns continue in zigzag
fashion. We have continued for about two hundred
meters along the convoluted course of the water
without knowing where it would lead. And we two
have met like lost creatures in the middle of a vast
rice paddy. There is nothing to be seen clearly but
the rain. My uncle slightly raises the brim of his hat
and looks up at the sky. It is austere and closed in like
the cover of a tea jar. From this hermetically sealed
surface, the rain descends interminably. When one
stands upright, the noise is deafening. The sputtering
of the raindrops falling on the hat and the straw
cloak. The sound of the water falling from the clouds
on to the four corners of the rice field. The sound
seems to be augmented by the distant impact of the
rain on the forest surrounding the sanctuary of Kio,[8]
which can be seen on the other side.

Overhanging the forest, the black clouds gather
together in the boundless sky, responding to the call
of the high branches of the cryptomers. They bend
further and further downwards with their own
weight. They seem to become entangled with the
foliage, dark "wadding" winding itself around the
crowns of the great trees. It seems as it they are
about to crash down into the forest.

Returning to reality, I notice that the water is flowing continuously upstream. The pond behind the Kio
sanctuary, no doubt assailed by the finally bursting

---

[8] This is doubtless the Inari Kio sanctuary in Tokyo, situated in
what is now the district of Shinjyuku, not far from the place
where Sōseki lived in his youth.

clouds, appears to have come alive, and the entire surface of the water is full of swirling eddies. My uncle once more observes their ascending motion, and in the tones of a man who has already caught something, says "Good fishing!" Very soon, without taking off his straw cape, he goes into the water. Compared with the violence of the current, the water is not very deep. It reaches more or less up to one's waist. My uncle takes up his position in the middle of the river, exactly opposite the wood of the Kio sanctuary, facing upstream, and lets the landing net slip off his shoulders.

Both motionless in the resounding rain, we look at the eddies pushing against us. There is no doubt that the fish are passing underneath them, carried along from the Kio pond by the violence of the current. "With a little luck we may catch a big one!" I think, keeping my eyes fixed on the dark color of the water. It is in greater turmoil than ever. It is impossible to decide, from the mere movement of the surface, what is going on in the depths. However, I see my uncle, without batting an eyelid, standing in the water up to his waist, and I wait to see a trembling in his wrists. But they remain perfectly still.

The curtain of rain becomes more and more dense. The color of the river gradually darkens. The contours of the eddies swirl at an increasingly violent rhythm. At this moment, in a wave as black as night, distinctly moving before my eyes, I seem to see a fleeting glow—a strangely colored shape. It strikes me as elongated and, for a split second, scintillating. "There's a nice eel!" I think to myself.

At the same moment, and against the current, my uncle's right wrist, holding the handle of the landing net, moves upwards, raising the straw cape up to his shoulder, in such a rapid movement that it seems to me about to turn over. The elongated shape then escapes from my uncle's hand. Tracing a curved trajectory in the torrential rain, it drops on to the opposite bank like a heavy rope. This is followed by the astonishing sight of the head of a snake, extending to about thirty centimeters above the grass. It fixed us with a menacing look.

"We shall meet again!"

There is no doubt that it is my uncle's voice. At the same moment, the head descends into the grass. My uncle, who has gone very pale, continues to gaze towards the spot where he has flung the snake.

"Uncle, was that you who said just now 'We shall meet again!'?"

Slowly, he turns towards me. Then, in an undertone, he answers that he does not exactly know. To this day, whenever I remind my uncle of this incident, he assures me, with a curious expression on his face, that he really does not know who uttered those words.

3
The Thief

Retiring for the night, I went into the next room, where the odor of the *kotatsu*[9] assailed my nostrils. On returning from the toilet, I pointed out to my wife that the heating was excessive and advised her to be careful. I then went to my room. It was past eleven o'clock. At first, as usual, I enjoyed calm dreams. It was cold, even though there was no wind, and I heard no bells ringing. I sank into a deep sleep that blotted out all sense of time.

I was suddenly woken by the servant crying. It is a habit of hers to burst into tears when any shock disturbs her. It appears that the other day, when she was bathing our youngest, he became extremely flushed and suffered convulsions. She cried for a whole five minutes while giving us an account of the incident. It was the first time I had heard our servant's voice, which, to say the least, was peculiar. The words tumbled out, every one of them aspirated, the entire content accompanied by plaintive inflections resembling supplications, as imploring forgiveness or moaning the loss of something dear to her—in short, quite unlike the short, sharp exclamations with which emotion is normally expressed.

As I said, I was woken by the singular voice I have just described. There is no doubt that it was coming from the room next to my wife's bedroom. At the same time, the incandescent light of the fire was filtering through the *fusuma*,[10] temporarily lighting up

---

[9] A heating system built into part of the floor.
[10] A sliding door.

my study. As soon as the red glow had penetrated my eyelids and reached my retina, I jumped up. Thinking a fire must have broken out, I hurriedly opened the canvas partition separating my room from the next.

At the same time, I had visions of an upset stove and a burnt eiderdown, I visualized curls of smoke and *tatami*[11] in flames. But the moment the partition, hastily pushed by me, slammed open, I saw the lamp burning in the usual manner. My wife and the children were peacefully asleep. The stove was in the right place, just as it had been the evening before. Nothing that I had seen on retiring for the night had changed. Peace reigned everywhere in the house. It was filled with a warm atmosphere. The servant alone was weeping.

On taking a closer look, I saw the servant clinging to the end of my wife's couch and heard her stammering. My wife opened her eyes and her lids fluttered once or twice, but she did not seem to wake up properly. Understanding practically nothing of what was happening, I remained rooted to the spot, peering into every part of the room. Then, in the middle of the maid's tearful report, I was able to make out the word "thief". Hardly had this reached my ears than everything seemed to become clear. I rapidly crossed my wife's room and rushed into the room adjacent to it, shouting, "Who's there?" But the room was plunged in darkness. To one side was the kitchen, of which one shutter was open, the full light of the moon penetrating as far as the door leading into the dark room. The moonlight pervading the back of the house made my blood run cold. Without shoes or slippers, I went on as far as the floored part,

[11]A straw mat.

but once I had reached the sink there was complete silence. Outside there was only the moon to be seen. I was not in the least keen to go on through the door.

I did an about-face and went to calm my wife, telling her that the thief had taken flight and that nothing was missing. She had finally got up without saying a word. She grasped a lamp, went into the darkened room, holding the flame above a chest of drawers. The doors had been removed and the drawers opened. My wife looked at me and said, "We've been robbed!" I, in turn, concluded that the thief had taken flight after he had committed the crime. And then everything suddenly struck me as absurd. I cast a glance to one side and noticed that the couch of the servant who had come to warn us in tears was unfolded. At the head of the couch there was another chest of drawers on which a small article of furniture had been placed. My wife explained to me that among the other contents of the drawers there was the cash for the doctor's fees for the year about to end. She herself made sure that everything was in order. It was from the veranda that the maid had come running in tears, and it was possible that the thief, taken by surprise, had left his handiwork unfinished.

In the end, the entire household was awake. They all left their rooms and all wanted to make themselves heard. "When I think that a moment earlier I had got up to go and relieve myself!" or "I could not get to sleep until two o'clock in the morning!" Each complained in his own particular way. In the middle of it all, my eldest daughter, who is ten years old, declared that she had seen and heard everything. She claimed to know that the thief had obtained access via the window, and that she had heard the floor of the veranda creaking as he walked over it. "Good heavens!" exclaimed our relative O-Fusa, who was eighteen and was sharing my eldest daughter's room. As for me, I went back to bed and fell asleep.

Owing to all this commotion, I got up the following morning a little later than usual. I washed and dressed, and while I was having my breakfast the servant was creating a real commotion in the kitchen, crying that footprints had been found, and then that they were not those of the thief after all, and so on. I retired to my study, finding all this disturbing. After ten minutes at the most, I heard a voice ringing out in the entrance hall, "If you please!" in decided tones. The kitchen staff had apparently not heard anyone, so I went myself. I found a policeman standing in front of the entrance. "I hear you had a burglary," he said with a smile. "But was everything properly locked?" "No, I don't think so," I replied. "Well then," he pointed out to me, "It's bound to happen. Unless all the entries and exits are properly closed, they get in anywhere—you must make sure you latch each shutter!" I assented, although with little conviction. Faced with this policeman, I began to think it was not the burglar who was at fault but the householder who did not take sufficient care to lock up.

The sergeant went through the house and then made for the kitchen. He asked my wife to tell him exactly what was missing and listed the items in his notebook. "You say, a 'satin ceremonial belt, with embroidery'. What exactly do you mean by 'ceremonial belt'?" I suppose it will be all right if I simply put down 'embroidered satin'? I see, all right. So, let's say 'a belt', and then...."

The maid wore a mocking smile. This policeman

did not know the difference between an ordinary belt and a ceremonial belt. His simplicity was really amusing. Shortly afterwards, the list of stolen objects was complete, and there seemed to be about ten; underneath each one he had entered its value, and he then stated, as he was about to depart, "So altogether, that makes a hundred and fifty yen!"

I now know exactly what was stolen. Ten objects: belts only. Our intruder of yesterday evening thus specializes in belts! My wife, thinking of the forth-coming New Year's Day, was looking depressed. It seemed that the children would be unable to change their kimonos on the first three days of the New Year. What could I do about it?

At the beginning of the afternoon, an inspector came to see us. He entered the living room and looked everywhere. He wondered whether the intruder had not perhaps made use of some vessel as a support for a lighted candle, and he even examined the little bowls in the kitchen. I offered him a cup of tea and invited him to sit in the *cha-no-ma*,[12] which has the advantage of being on the sunny side. We then chatted.

Apparently, thieves generally arrive by tram from Shitaya or the environs of Asakusa and leave the next day, again by tram. This means that they are practi-cally never caught. Again, even if one is arrested it seems that it is the inspector who is the loser. For he has to pay for his tram ticket, and if the culprit is taken to court he has to be given a cold meal. The police prefecture appropriates half the secret funds. The rest is distributed among the commissariats. At Ushigome there are only three or four inspectors.

[12] The main room of the house, used as the living room.

Having been convinced that everything, or almost everything, was possible with the help of the police, I felt very depressed. The inspector who told me this appeared equally disheartened.

As I wanted to repair the locks of our home, I expected to put the work in the hands of someone who knew the house well, but as it was the end of the year he had too much in hand and was unable to come. The day drew to a close and night came on. We had to make the best of the situation and went to bed after tidying up. Nobody in the house felt reassured. I myself likewise felt uneasy. How could I feel at ease after the kind of warning given to me by the police, who laid on every householder the responsibility for ensuring his own security?

However, this did not prevent me from retiring for the night, moderately relieved at the idea that this time we had nothing to fear, having been burgled the night before. Once more, however, I was woken by my wife in the middle of the night. She said that a moment ago she had heard scratching sounds coming from the kitchen. She was not reassured and asked me to get up and go and find out the cause. It is true that an unaccustomed noise was to be heard. From the expression on my wife's face, she seemed convinced that a thief had broken in.

I got up, being careful not to make any noise. I proceeded gingerly through my wife's bedroom, and when I reached the *fusuma* which separated it from the next room I heard the servant's snores. I slid the partitions back as silently as possible and continued as far as the middle of the room, which was plunged in darkness. There was certainly a continual clicking sound to be heard. There was undoubtedly something at the entrance to the kitchen. As silent as a shadow, I took three steps in the direction of the noise and very soon reached the end of the room. I brushed against a paper partition. Beyond it was a floored corridor. Going right up to the *shōji*[13] I listened attentively to what was occurring in the dark. Very soon I heard a scratching sound. After a minute the strange noise started again and was repeated four or five times. It came from the left of the floored part. After discovering that the scratching was, in actual fact, coming from the back of a cupboard, I returned to my wife's bedroom, once more walking in the normal manner. When I had assured her that it was only something being gnawed by a mouse, she relaxed and thanked me. We then calmly went back to sleep.

In the morning, after washing my face as usual, I had hardly arrived in the *cha-no-ma* when my wife came and stood in front of my breakfast tray, waving in front of my face the *katsuobushi*[14] at which the mouse had been gnawing the evening before. I looked at the piece of dried bonito fish which had suffered merciless nibbling throughout the night. My wife said, a little reproachfully, "All the same, you could have taken the opportunity of chasing the mouse away and putting the dried bonito back in its place!" Now that she had pointed it out to me, I realized a little late that this was certainly what I ought to have done.

[13] Sliding partition of which the thin wooden latticework is covered with paper.
[14] A fish which is dried and flaked and used in Japanese cookery.

4
The Persimmon

The little girl's name is Kii-chan. She has velvety skin and lively eyes, but her cheeks do not shine with the good health of the children in the neighborhood, who grow without problems. When one looks at her, one immediately notices her yellowish complexion. Our hairdresser once said this was the fault of her mother, who was overprotective and did not let her go and enjoy herself outside. That hairdresser, at a time when hair coiled in the Western manner is the fashion, keeps to the old hairstyle, renewing it every four days, and when she calls her little girl she never fails to add the courtesy suffix at the end of the name. There is another lady older than her and with the hairstyle adopted by widows. This is the grandmother, and she too calls out "*Kii-chan! Kii-chan!*" She calls, "It's time for your *kōto*[15] lesson," or else, "Kii-chan, don't go out playing with the neighbors' children!" and so forth.

This is why the little girl is hardly ever able to go out and play in the street. It must be admitted that it is not a particularly good area. A man who makes rice cakes lives opposite. Next door there is a tile maker. A little further on there is a shop selling straps for clogs, and then a tinker, who also repairs locks. As for Kii-chan's father, he is a government employee who works in a bank. Behind the surrounding wall of the house, there is a pine tree. At the approach of winter, a gardener comes to gather up

---

[15] A kind of long, horizontal harp with thirteen strings.

the dead pine needles and uses them to cover the beds of the little garden.

When Kii-chan comes home from school and starts to get bored, she goes out to play, although a little reluctantly, at the back of the house. That is where her mother and grandmother starch the washing and put it out to dry. It is also the place where the washing is done and where, at the end of the year, men wearing black headbands come to pound steamed rice in a mortar to make rice cake. Not forgetting the salted vegetables stored in barrels.

As soon as Kii-chan arrives, either her mother or her grandmother stops work, both being transformed into playmates. Sometimes the little girl finds nobody there to play with. She goes there all the same, and through the gaps in the little quickset hedge separating the house from the street she gazes for a long time at the *nagaya*[16] behind the house.

There are five or six houses in a row under one roof. There is a bank nearly a meter high along the quickset hedge, so that from her "observation post" Kii-chan is just at the right height for keeping watch. She takes a little child's delight in dominating the row of houses in this way. When Tatsu, who works in the ornaments factory, takes a drink of saké, naked to the waist, she announces this with the words, "Mother, he's having a drink!" When Genbō the carpenter sharpens his hatchet, she says, "Grandmother, he's sharpening something!" And she reports a number of other things, such as, "They're having an argument!" or "They're eating roast potatoes!" She faithfully passes on everything she has seen and heard. And she bursts out laughing. Then her mother and

[16] Rows of linked houses.

grandmother join in. Kii-chan thus has a gift for amusing people.

While Kii-chan is watching the row of houses, she and Yokichi, Genbō's little boy, happen to catch sight of each other. And every so often they start talking. But it goes without saying that the two children never agree. It always ends in a quarrel. From down below Yokichi calls out, "Look at the pale moon-face!" This is answered from above by the words "Little jerk!" and the little girl juts out her chin with an air of disdain for the boy from a poor family. Yokichi once got angry and brandished a washing pole. This frightened Kii-chan, who retreated indoors. Another time Yokichi at first refused to return the pretty rubber ball covered in wool[17] which Kii-chan had dropped from the top of the hedge. "Let me have my ball back! Please!" she implored at the top of her voice. But Yokichi, with the ball in his hands, just stayed there and looked up at her with an air of superiority. "Then say you're sorry! If you do, I'll give it back." Kii-chan's reply was, "I apologize to you? Never! Thief!" and without awaiting his reply she went back to her mother, who was at work, and burst into tears. Her mother took the matter to heart and in a very matter-of-fact way sent someone to fetch the ball. But Yokichi's mother simply said there was unfortunately nothing she could do, and Kii-chan never recovered her plaything.

Three days later, Kii-chan once again turned up at the back of the house, this time carrying an enormous orange-colored persimmon. In his usual

---

[17] At that time, little girls were in the habit of covering balls with a kind of plaited network of woolen threads in a wide variety of colors.

manner, Yokichi came over to the bottom of the embankment. Kii-chan, passing the red fruit through the hedge, said,"Would you like it?" Yokichi, giving it a sidelong glance, replied, "Why should I want you to give it to me? In honor of what? However, he did not go away. "You don't want it? Oh, all right, then." And Kii-chan withdrew her hand. Yokichi then started to threaten her, saying, "What are you on about? I'm going to beat you!" He was moving closer and closer to the bank. "So you would like it?" said Kii-chan, showing him the persimmon once more. "Like it? Me, want a thing like that! I don't think so!" Yet he looked upwards, wide-eyed.

After this scene had been repeated four or five times, Kii-chan said, "Well, now you can have it!" and she then threw the persimmon, which got squashed at the bottom of the hedge. Yokichi rushed over and seized the fruit, which was all covered in mud. Then, without wasting any more time, he bit into it with gusto.

At this moment, Yokichi's nostrils started to quiver. His mouth, with its fleshy lips, were stretched to one side in a tremendous grimace. He spat the fruit out. Then, giving her a look in which all the hate of which he was capable was concentrated, he yelled, "You knew it couldn't be eaten, didn't you?"[18] He then flung the damaged fruit at Kii-chan. The persimmon passed over her head and hit the sloping roof. The little girl cried, "Ha ha! That will teach you to be greedy!" and ran back indoors. Bursts of laughter could soon be heard in Kii-chan's house.

---

[18] It was probably of the *shibugaki* variety, which has a bitter taste making it inedible, in contrast to the other variety, the *amagaki*, which is very popular.

5
The Brazier

When I opened my eyes, I found that the hot water bottle which I had laid on my stomach on going to bed the night before had gone cold. I saw the gray sky, looking as if it were covered with a heavy leaden sheet. My stomach pains seemed to have gone. Making a determined movement, I sat upright but found it to be much colder than I had imagined. Under the window, the snow which had fallen the day before lay thick and undisturbed upon the ground.

The freezing bathroom seems covered with a shiny glaze. The water is frozen and the tap is not working. Not without an effort, I succeed in rubbing myself down with a hot towel, and when I enter the *cha-no-ma* to pour myself a cup of tea, my son, who is two years old, starts crying. This has definitely become a habit. The day before yesterday again, without a pause. I asked my wife what was the matter with him, and she replied that there was nothing wrong and that he was simply crying with the cold. There is nothing we can do about it. Nor are his tears sad or desperate, and he is content to snivel. Still, since he is crying, there is something that is causing him to suffer. Listening to his groans, I myself feel distressed. At certain moments I am exasperated. I feel like shouting at him, but then I tell myself that in spite of it all he is too little to be given a scolding, and I end up by controlling my feelings. It was like this yesterday and the day before. At the prospect of a repetition today, from the morning onwards, I am not in the best of moods. But as I have a weak stomach, I have for some time past made it a rule to eat nothing at all for breakfast, so I take my cup of tea and retire with it to my study.

I stretch my hands over the brazier. When they are a little warmer, the crying on the other side can still be heard. After a moment, only the palms of my hands feel hot—so much so that one would almost have expected to see smoke coming out of them. My back and shoulders, however, are numb with cold. My toes are so icy, furthermore, that it is positively painful. I remain helpless and motionless. The slightest movement of my hand causes me to touch something cold. And this sensation affects my nerves as if they have been stabbed by thorns. Merely moving my head is unbearable when I feel the icy cold collar of my kimono touch the nape of my neck. Assailed by the cold from all sides, I curl up inside my ten *tatami*. Only the carpet is not very big—it measures only sixty centimeters—and the floor left bare is shiny and smooth. While in my motionless "huddle", gazing at the wooden slats, the little fellow goes on crying. I lack the courage to work.

At this moment, my wife bursts into my study, and while apologizing for taking my watch tells me that it has started snowing again. I look up and see that light snowflakes have started to fall, which at first I had not noticed. From the stormy sky, with no wind to disperse the clouds, the impassive snowflakes fall slowly and gently.

"Last year, by the way, when one of the children fell ill, we lit the stove. Do you remember what we paid for the coal?"

"At the end of that month I paid twenty-eight yen."

Hearing my wife's reply, I give up my momentary idea of lighting the stove. It remains in a corner of the lean-to at the rear of the house.

"I say, couldn't you get the child to make a little less noise?"

The expression on my wife's face is one of helplessness. She then says, "O-masa says she has pains in her stomach. She really seems to be suffering and I was thinking it would be just as well to send for Dr Hayashi. What do you think?"

I know that O-masa has been in bed for two or three days, but I had no idea it was so serious. I urge my wife to send for the doctor as soon as possible. She assures me she will see to it at once and leaves my study, taking my watch with her. Closing the *fusuma*, she exclaims, "This room really is freezing!"

I am still shivering with the cold and feel no urge to get down to work. The truth is that I do not know where to start. I have to edit an article for the paper. I have promised to read two or three short stories sent to me by an unknown young man who would like to know my opinion of them. I have promised to write a letter to be sent with somebody's work and recommending it. The books I am supposed to have been reading in the course of these two or three months are piling up on my desk like a mountain.

For a whole week now, whenever I have sat down at my desk with the firm intention of tackling these tasks, people have called on me. Everybody comes to consult me on one thing or another. To crown it all, I am having stomach trouble. So today I am fasting. But it is no good telling me that I should get some exercise. The cold is unendurable. I have no heart for anything and cannot take my hands away from the brazier.

At this moment, I hear the sound of a carriage, which stops by the house. The servant comes in. "Mr Nagasawa is here," she announces, and she shows him in. I remain crouched over the brazier and tell him I am too cold to move. Nagasawa then takes a letter out of his kimono and starts to read it to me. On the 15th of this month, corresponding to the first day of the year by the old calendar, I am urgently asked for something. As always, it is a question of money. Nagasawa leaves after midday. But it is still too cold to cope with anything. In the state I am in, I tell myself, it would be better to plunge into a really hot bath in order to recover a little vigor, but as soon as I get to the hall, holding my towel, I find myself face to face with Yoshida. I return with him to the living room, and he tells me all about his affairs—and all of a sudden he starts to cry, the tears rolling down his cheeks. A few minutes later, the doctor comes and a commotion can be heard at the back of the house. When Yoshida finally takes his departure, my little boy starts crying again. Then, at long last, I am able to go and have my bath.

When I come out of the bathhouse, I feel warm for the first time that day. With an airy tread, I return to the house and enter my study. The lamp is on and the curtains are drawn. The charcoal in the brazier has been topped up. I sit down somewhat heavily on my cushion. My wife then arrives from the back of the house with a bowl of soup, thinking I must be feeling cold. I ask about O-masa, and my wife tells me that she may turn out to have appendicitis. I take the bowl of soup from her hands and say that if it turns out to be necessary we will have to take her to hospital. She naturally agrees with me. Soon afterwards, she goes back to the *cha-no-ma*.

After my wife has left the room, everything suddenly turns silent. It is a really snowy evening. Fortunately, the little lad has fallen asleep and the crying has stopped. Taking little gulps of the hot liquid by the light of the lamp, I listen to the cracking of the live charcoal, the red flames flickering amid the imprisoned embers. Now and again, a bluish spark escapes. The sight of the fire gives me the feeling, for the first time, that it has been a nice day. For a long time, I continue to gaze at the gradually whitening embers.

6
The Boarding House

My first lodgings were situated at a certain height in the northern part of the town. The red brick house with one single story appealed to me at once with its peaceful appearance, and this is what made me decide to take the accommodation despite the comparatively high charge, which was two pounds a week for a back room. Mr K..., who at that time reigned over the entire front of the house, was traveling all over Scotland at the time, and according to the landlady, he would not be back for some time.

The lady of the house had sharp features, with sunken eyes, a *retroussé* nose, a pointed chin and prominent cheekbones. She was so far beyond any femininity that it was impossible, on first seeing her, to guess her age. All the human weaknesses— bitterness, envy, obstinacy, rigidity, doubt—must have taken a delight in playing with that face to give it that ill-favored appearance. Such was my particular impression.

Her black hair and black eyes seemed out of place in these northern climes. Her speech, however, in no way differed from that of English people. The day I moved in, I was called, from downstairs, to go down for tea. I descended the stairs and found that no other member of the family was present. I was alone with the lady of the house in the narrow dining room that faced north. I looked round the gloomy dining room, which the sunlight never seemed to enter, and noticed on the mantelpiece a vase containing lifeless-looking narcissi. While handing me my tea and toast, she started to talk about this and that. At the end of the conversation, she took the opportunity of informing me that her native country was not England, but France. Then, turning her black eyes towards the narcissi withering in the glass vase, she added that England, a cold and cloudy country, was not a pleasant place to live in. No doubt she intended to point out to me that in this country even the flowers failed to bloom.

For my part, silently comparing the narcissi which had bloomed so feebly with the pallor of this woman's hollow cheeks, I imagined the sweet dreams that thoughts of faraway France must have brought into her mind. How many vain springs must have come and gone, leaving behind nothing but an evanescent perfume of the past concealed behind her black hair and black eyes? I wanted to know whether she spoke French. Before even taking the time to answer "no", she uttered two or three sentences in the flowing language of the south. I was amazed to hear such a beautiful accent from that emaciated throat.

That evening, a bald, elderly man with a white beard took his place at the dinner table. After the spinster had informed me that he was her father, I noticed that my host was an old man. He had a curious way of expressing himself. It was immediately obvious that he was not English. I gathered that father and daughter had crossed the Channel to settle in England. Then, as if purposely anticipating my enquiry, he told me he was German. The facts were different from what I had imagined, and I simply replied, "OK, I see," without adding anything else.

After I had gone back to my room, I started to read, but my thoughts were strangely taken up with the father and daughter who I knew were downstairs.

They bore not the slightest resemblance to each other—where her face was angular, his was moon-shaped, with a fleshy nose in the middle, and two little eyes above it. It reminded me of Kruges, the President of the South African Republic. It was not the kind of face one is delighted to encounter. There was also no pleasantness in his voice when he addressed his daughter. His teeth no longer obeyed him, so that he was obliged to mutter, yet there was still a roughness in his tones. His daughter's severe visage seemed to become still more so when she spoke to her father. I was completely unable to believe that their relations were normal. Such were the thoughts that filled my mind that night when I went to sleep.

Next morning when I came down to breakfast, there was another person at the table beside the father and daughter who had been present the evening before. The newcomer was a man of about forty years of age with a bright complexion and a welcoming manner. When I entered the dining room and saw his face, I at last felt I was in the company of living human beings. The woman performed the introduction. She just said, "My brother!" As I expected, he was not her husband. But their two faces were so different that it would have been almost impossible for anyone to take them for brother and sister.

I lunched in town that day and returned to the boarding house at about three o'clock. I had hardly reached my room when I was called down for tea. Once again, it was a dull day. When I opened the door of the dingy dining room, I found the lady of the house seated alone by the stove and holding a cup. As the stove had been lit, the room became a little more cheerful looking. The fire from the stove lit up the woman's countenance, and I saw that her slightly red cheeks had been powdered, almost imperceptibly. Standing in the doorway, I became profoundly aware of the loneliness hidden by the face powder. She gave me a look that seemed to imply that she had discerned my thoughts. This was the day she told me her family history.

Her mother had married a Frenchman twenty-five years before, and a daughter had been born of this union. After a few years of marriage, the husband had died. She had remarried, her second husband being a German, and this was the elderly man I had met the evening before. He now kept a tailor's shop in the West End of London and went there every day. His son by a first marriage also worked in the shop, but there was an unusual degree of dissension between them, so much so that, although living under the same roof, they never spoke to each other. The son invariably came home at a late hour. He took his shoes off just inside the door, went along the corridor in his socks in order not to be heard by his father, entered his room and went to bed. The woman's own mother had been dead for some considerable time. Before she died, she had implored her husband to look after her daughter, but the entire fortune which she left finally went to the stepfather, and her daughter did not receive a penny. It was in order to earn a little money, that she had resigned herself to opening a boarding house.

She did not tell me any more. Agnes was a girl of thirteen or fourteen who helped in the house. I then thought I noticed a vague resemblance between the son whom I had seen that morning and the young girl. The latter had just arrived from the kitchen carrying the toast.

"Agnes, would you like a piece of toast?"

Without saying a word, the girl took the offered piece of toast and disappeared in the direction of the kitchen.

A month later, I left the boarding house.

7
Odor of the Past

About two weeks before I left the boarding house, K... returned from Scotland. It was the lady of the house who undertook the introductions. When two Japanese who have met by chance in a little house in a London suburb become acquainted and bow to each other in the presence of a lady who knows nothing of their respective positions, natures or occupations, this strikes me, now that I come to think of it, as somewhat unusual. On the day in question, she was wearing black. With a gesture that made her thin, dried-up hands particularly noticeable, she began, "Mr K..., this is Mr N...", and before even finishing her sentences, touching her interlocutor with her other hand, continued, "Mr N..., allow me to introduce Mr K...!"—thus taking care to maintain equality.

Her salesman-like attitude, with an evident desire to attach due importance to formality, could not but cause me astonishment. While looking at me, K... gave a hint of a smile, thus creasing the borders of his attractive double eyelids. For my part, I did not feel like smiling, being all too conscious of the melancholy side of this artificial situation. Standing opposite K..., I told myself that my feeling must be similar to that which might be caused at a wedding by the presence of a ghost in the place of the intermediary! I had the impression that everything that moved within the dark shadow of this prematurely faded spinster lost its vitality and was transformed into a ruin. I could not help thinking that if one accidentally brushed against that flesh, the blood would freeze at the exact point where contact had occurred and nowhere else. I turned towards the door, which she had just closed, and heard her steps receding.

After she had left us, K... and I immediately became close friends. The floor of his room was covered with a fine carpet, and there were white muslin curtains over the windows. In addition to a magnificent couch and a rocking chair, he had a separate little bedroom. But the most welcome feature of all was the stove, which remained permanently alight, devouring the plentiful and still burning embers.

From then onwards, I developed the habit of coming to have tea in K...'s apartment, where he and I were quite alone. We often went to lunch together in a restaurant nearby. It was always K... who paid the bill. I understood that he had come to England to carry out research in connection with harbor construction, and he was by no means short of money. Indoors he wore an orange-colored satin dressing gown, and appeared highly content with his position. I myself wore the same clothes that I had on when leaving Japan. They were all dirty, and I cut a shabby figure compared with him. Surmising that I was down-at-heel, K... lent me the money to have a new suit made.

A fortnight later, K... and I started discussing a wide variety of matters. He informed me about one of his plans, which consisted of the creation of a ministerial cabinet under the name of "the Keio cabinet". He explained the reason for this choice: all the future members would have to have been born during the era of the same name. "By the way, what year were you born in?" he asked. It so happened that I was born in the third year of the Keio era. K... then laughingly informed me that I was eligible to become a member of his cabinet. As far as I can remember, he himself had been born in the first or second year. I only escaped by one year being unable to join K... on the team which would direct the affairs of the State!

During such light-hearted talks, we would sometimes touch on the family that occupied the ground floor. K... then never failed to shake his head and frown. It was little Agnes he was most sorry for. As soon as morning comes, she carries coal up to K...'s room. In the afternoon, she brings him tea and toast. She arrives silently, puts everything down silently and departs silently. She is always pale, and her only greeting is a movement of her damp eyes. She appears like a shadow and departs like a shadow. Her footsteps are never heard.

One day, I told K... that I intended to leave the boarding house, where I felt ill at ease. He approved of my decision, adding that he himself, with the frequent changes of address necessitated by his research activities, had no objection to staying, but that in my case it was certainly preferable to be able to study in peace and in more comfortable quarters. K... then made his preparations for a trip, which was to take him to the far side of the Mediterranean.

When I informed her of my intended departure, the proprietress pressed me to stay. She went as far as to promise to lower her charges, and even told me that I could have K...'s room while he was away. I nevertheless left the boarding house and took lodgings in one of the southerly districts of the town. At the same time, K... was preparing for his long voyage.

Two or three months later, I heard from K... unexpectedly. He had returned from his travels. "I am not about to move very far away, so do come and see me!" he wrote. I would very much like to have done so, but a great many things prevented me from finding the time to cross London. After about a week, taking advantage of something I had to do in Islington, I made a detour before going home, in order to call on K....

The muslin curtains were reflected in the windowpanes on the first floor. I was looking forward to the travel anecdotes which K..., always so dynamic, would not fail to relate to me. In my mind's eye, I saw the stove, the embroidered orange-colored satin dressing gown and the couch, and passed resolutely through the gate. I rapidly mounted the steps and gave two raps with the knocker. There was no sound from inside. Thinking that I had not been heard, I was about to knock once more when the door opened, as if by itself. I stepped into the apartment. I found myself face to face with Agnes, who raised apologetic eyes. At this moment, the odor of the boarding house in which I had been staying previously, and which henceforward belonged to the past, that odor which for three months I had forgotten, assailed my senses like a flash of lightning as I stood there in the corridor. This odor was permeated with the secret that weighed upon the occupants, the black hair, the black eyes, the face of the man who resembled Kruger and whose son resembled Agnes, who seemed to be his shadow. On noticing this odor, I became acutely conscious of the fact that their feelings, their gestures, their words, and their physiognomy belonged to the hell of secrets. My courage forsook me. I turned and went away....

8
The Cat's Grave

As soon as we moved to Waseda, the cat began to waste away visibly. He shows not the least desire to play with the children. When the veranda is warmed by the sun, that is where he sleeps. With his front paws neatly stretched out before him, he rests his square face on top of them and remains motionless in this position for any length of time, his eyes fixed on the plants in the garden. The children play around him in vain, ignored by him as far as they are concerned. They decided at the very beginning not to bother about him. On the grounds that he will prove useless as a playmate, they leave him alone of their own accord. But it is not only to the children that he has ceased to be of interest. The servant, too, simply places a plate in a corner of the kitchen three times a day. Apart from this, she ignores him, so to speak. Furthermore, the food given to him is in most cases swallowed by a big white, black and brown cat in the neighborhood. But he never seems inclined to get angry. I have never seen him fighting. He simply lies there motionless and asleep. Even when he is lying down, one has the impression that he has not the slightest margin for movement. He is not lying comfortably in order to be able to stretch out and take advantage of the sun; it is simply that he sees no reason to move. Yet, I realize that this description is inadequate. Let us say that he gives the impression of having exceeded the limits of indolence. Indeed, it must be said that if he is depressed at remaining motionless, he would be still more so at the idea of making a movement, and he therefore endures it with patience. His eyes seem to be fixed on what grows in the garden, but he has probably never been actually conscious of the leaves on the trees or the shape of the tree trunks. He has directed his yellowish-green pupils towards one fixed point. Just as his existence has not been recognized by my children, he himself ignores the existence of the world.

Despite all, he now and again has to go outside as if he has something to do. He is then pursued by the big tomcat from nearby and, as if afraid of him, he leaps on to the veranda in one single jump, traversing and destroying one of the *shōji* which serve as a partition and taking refuge in the *irori*.[19] It is only at these moments that the household notices his existence. As far as the cat himself is concerned, it is probably his only opportunity of being fully conscious that he exists.

Through the constant repetition of these incidents, the hairs on the cat's long tail have become sparse. At first there were isolated holes, but with the passing of time his loss of hair reached the point where one could see the skin all red, and this was a pitiful sight. He seemed to be at the end of his tether, constantly curled up into a ball in order to lick the sensitive places.

"Tell me, don't you think the cat has something wrong with him?" I asked my wife. "Yes, there is!" she replied in a tone of indifference "But what do you expect? It must be his age." I therefore let matters take their course without worrying about it any more. Then, after a certain time, the cat started to vomit. Enormous waves of matter passed up through his throat, from which distressing sounds could be

---

[19] A hearth built into the floor.

heard, neither a sneeze nor a hiccup. He seemed to be suffering, yet at the first sign of such a fit he was chased outside, otherwise he constantly soiled the *tatami* or the bedclothes. A silk cushion we had provided for a visitor was soiled by him in this way.

"It's getting annoying! Something has to be done! He must have some intestinal disorder or something wrong with his stomach. You ought to try giving him Hōtan diluted in a little water."

My wife did not answer. Two or three days later, I asked her whether she had given the cat the powder mentioned. "I certainly tried, but he refuses to open his mouth!" she replied. She then went on to explain, "When I give him fish bones, he vomits."

"Well then, you mustn't give them to him any more!" I went on reading after roughly reproaching my wife.

When the cat was not vomiting, he slept peacefully as usual. Towards the end, he became shrivelled and—as if only the veranda would bear his weight—he curled up in order to reduce the length of his body as far as possible. His expression had undergone a hardly perceptible change. At first, like his eyes, which by fixing themselves on a distant point were lost in a kind of haze, his glance was imbued with a sort of serenity as long as he remained motionless, but little by little he had undergone a disquieting change. At the same time, the iris clouded over more and more. His look was like the dusk lit up by a faint flash of lightning. However, I did nothing about it, and nor did my wife concern herself about him in the least—to say nothing of the children, who had actually forgotten his existence.

One evening, while lying on the children's bedding, the cat gave a moan like the one he let out when we tried to make him release a fish he had managed to seize in his mouth. At that moment, I was the only one who noticed and worried about it. The children were sound asleep. A moment later, the cat gave another moan, and my wife finally put down her needle. I said, "What's the matter with him? Don't you see he'll start biting the children? On the head, for instance. How can I know?"

"Do you really think so?" and my wife went on sewing the sleeves of an under-kimono. From time to time, the cat moaned again.

The next morning, he climbed on to the edge of the *irori* and stayed there the whole day, plaintively miaowing all the time. He appeared to be disturbed when we gave him tea or came to get the kettle. By the evening, my wife and I had forgotten about the cat altogether and it was on that evening that he died. In the morning, when the servant went to fetch wood from the lean-to at the back of the house, she found him lying rigid on the old earthenware stove.

My wife wanted to see the cat and went to the shed for this express purpose. Although until then she had proved totally indifferent, she was now sobbing. She sent for a carter whose services we had used in the past, asked him to go and purchase a wooden commemorative plaque, then came and asked me to add some inscription. On one side I wrote "Here lies the cat." And on the other side "From this earth—who knows?—there will be a flash of lightning as evening draws on." The carter asked whether he could bury the cat just as he was. The servant's riposte was, "Because you would like to incinerate him, perhaps?"

The children, in their turn, showed the cat every consideration. They placed flowers on each side on the commemorative plaque—sprays of lespedezas in glass vessels. They filled a bowl with water and placed it in front of the tomb. The flowers and the water were renewed the next morning and the morning after. At the end of the third day, I was looking through my study window and saw my daughter, who was nearly four years old, go over to the little tomb by herself and stand there for a moment or two looking at the plaque. She took out a little rice dish, poured over it some water from the bowl which had been used for the cat, and drank some of the contents. She then repeated her actions. The drops of water containing petals shed by the lespedezas in the quiet of the dusk have many a time passed down little Aiko's throat and slated her thirst.

On the anniversary of the day when the cat expired, my wife never fails to place a piece of salmon and a bowl of rice sprinkled with *katsuobushi* in front of his grave. So far she has not once forgotten to do this. But recently it seems that, instead of going out to the garden, she is content to place all this on the dressing table in the *cha-no-ma*.

9
A Sweet Dream

The wind beat against the high buildings, and as it could not escape by the same route, it moved in a sharp curve like a flash of lightning and took its final slanting course down to the pavements. While walking I held my top hat firmly on my head with my right hand. Ahead of me was a stationary carriage, obviously awaiting a passenger. Feeling sure that the driver was observing me from his seat, I let go of my hat, but I had hardly changed my position before he raised his forefinger. It was a sign to invite me to get in. But I did not do so. Then he began a vigorous beating of his chest with his right fist. The blows could even be heard a few meters away. This is how London coachmen warm themselves. I turned round to look at him for a moment or two. Bushy graying hair escaped from under his cap, which was hidden from view. With elbows stuck out, he raised his forearm with such an energetic movement that he almost touched the back of his brownish overcoat, which resembled a bundle of blankets, after which, raising his shoulders so that they formed a straight line, he vigorously beat his chest. His gestures were as regular as the movements of a machine. I continued on my way.

Everyone walking along the pavement overtook me—even the women. Placing their hands on their waists and slightly raising their skirts, they hurried along with their high heels tapping the pavement so sharply that they seemed to be in danger of snapping. If one observed the faces attentively, one noticed that they all had a strained expression. The men looked straight ahead, the women did not let their gaze wander to either side, and all were resolutely proceeding towards their chosen destinations. Their lips were tightly closed. Their eyebrows were so closely knit that they almost met in the middle. Their noses seemed to stick out and their faces to stretch forwards as if to keep ahead of the steps which bore them one after the other to their respective destinations. The way all of them were hurrying along created the impression that they felt ill at ease at the very fact that they were in the street, now that they had ventured out, and that they were desperately searching for some shelter to which they must repair if they were not to suffer the greatest disgrace of their lives.

For my part, proceeding at a casual pace, I vaguely thought that it must be hard to live in this capital city. I raised my head and looked at the immense sky which, partly obscured since I did not know whose reign, formed as it were, a long tight belt against the buildings rising to the right and left like cliffs. This "belt" had been mouse gray since the morning but was now gradually becoming speckled. The original color of the façades was ash gray, and the buildings, as if deeply disappointed by the feeble sunlight, had unrelentingly obstructed both sides. They had transformed the immense space into a dark, narrow ravine, and, in order to prevent them from being penetrated by the sun rising high in the sky, they had placed a further story over the ground floors, then a second and a third. The people, looking tiny, shivered as they passed along one side of this "ravine", like minute black dots. I myself was one of these atoms—the slowest of them all. Confined between the walls, the wind missed its exit route and rushed over the ravine as if to tear up the ground on its way. Like fish escaping from the meshes of the net, the black dots dispersed in all directions. Despite my slow gait, I myself was being pushed along by the wind, so I rapidly took shelter in one of the buildings.[20]

I first entered a long corridor and then ascended two or three steps of a stairway leading to a big swing door. As soon as I leaned against it, I was noiselessly and effortlessly propelled into the gallery. I was dazzled by the light around me. I turned round once more and found that the door had closed on its own and that the place where I now found myself was as peaceful as the spring. I blinked for a moment or two before my eyes became accustomed to the light. And then I looked around. To the left and right there were crowds of people. But they were all calm and silent, their facial muscles relaxed. They were all touching shoulders but this didn't seem to bother them, and they were in no way ill at ease in a crowd; rather, each seemed to relax the other. I looked upwards. The dome-shaped ceiling in its brilliant colors, with vivid gildings, which gleamed in a way that set my heart vibrating, left me in almost painful bedazzlement. I looked straight ahead. There was a banister the whole way along. Beyond it there was nothing to be seen, but only a gaping cavity. I went up to it, craned my neck and looked inside it. At a great distance the bottom was crowded with little beings that looked as if they had emerged from a picture. They were numerous—and yet so clear. It was exactly what is meant by a "sea of humanity". White, black, yellow, blue, violet, red—all the different colors undulated together in the distant background like the

[20] This is Her Majesty's Theatre, where Sōseki attended a performance of Shakespeare's *Twelfth Night.*

watery movements of the ocean, like tiny multi-colored shells of wonderful beauty.

At that moment, the spectacle suddenly vanished, giving way to a darkness that spread from the enormous cupola to the innermost depths. The people present, who could be counted in thousands, were swallowed up in the darkness. Everyone's existence, without exception, was effaced by the extreme darkness and they became as voiceless as if the shadows and shapes had disappeared. Then a good way ahead of me, part of the façade moved, revealing a rectangular space that almost imperceptibly lit up in the surrounding dark. At first I thought it was just a vague outline in the darkness, but little by little the blackness softened. When I became conscious of an actual glimmer of light, I was able to make out, by the rays of a beam of light as thin as mist, a range of opaque colors. Yellow, mauve, dark blue; very soon the yellow and the mauve started to move. While gazing so intently that my eyes grew tired, I stared unblinkingly at everything in motion. All of a sudden, the mist disappeared. Far off, on an expanse of greenery stretching out by the sea, sparkling under the hot rays of the sun, a handsome young man came in sight, wearing a yellow tunic and accompanied by a beautiful woman enveloped in a violet robe with long, billowing sleeves. When she sat down on a marble seat in the shade of an olive tree, the man remained standing and looked at her. Then, responding to the invitation of the warm wind that blew from the south, the peaceful sound of the orchestra came across the distant sea, its thin notes continuing without a pause.

The whole hall trembled at the same time. They had not disappeared in the darkness. In this darkness they were dreaming of Greece, which was all sweetness and light.

10
Impressions

When I crossed the threshold, I found myself in the big avenue passing the front of the house. I tried to take in the whole of it by standing in the middle of the road. All the houses in my field of vision were three-storied, and their façades were all the same color. The houses adjacent to mine, like the one opposite, were built in strictly the same style, and if after a few meters I made some attempt to retrace my steps, I could no longer tell which house I had come from. This is a very strange city.

Yesterday evening I went to sleep within earshot of the whistling of trains. Shortly after ten o'clock, I immersed myself in the night, as if in a dream, with its tapping footsteps and tinkling bells. At the same time, I perceived, without being fully conscious of it, a pleasant glow, repeated at various moments. Apart from that, I saw nothing while standing in this mysterious street.

I let my glance wander over the façades one by one, and after I had covered some two hundred meters I reached a crossroads, fixing everything firmly in my memory. I went to the right and found myself in a wider avenue than the one I had just left. Carriages were moving over it in all directions, with passengers on their roofs. Alternating red, yellow, green, brown and dark blue carriages passed by me in all directions and continued on their journeys. Where were all these colors bound? It would be very difficult for me to tell. If I turned round, they were coming towards me like many-colored clouds. My thoughts drew me into a labyrinth of conjecture in which the destination of all these travelers, taken up or set down by the carriages, remained a mystery, and I then felt my shoulders being pushed. Behind me I saw a tall man who almost eclipsed me. I tried to release myself but found a similar man on my right. On the left, the one who had pushed me was pushed in his turn by the man behind him. Nobody spoke and everyone proceeded onwards as if everything was normal.

For the first time, I had the feeling that I was engulfed in a sea of humanity. The extent of this ocean was as yet unknown to me. The waves, however, were calm, even if endless. It was simply that there could be no thought of escaping from it. I glanced to the right but saw no way out. I turned to the left, which likewise offered me no escape. I looked behind me. The space was hermetically sealed off. However, the movement, which took a forward direction, was tranquil. As if gripped by a fate from which there was no escape, I too progressed forward, adapting my step to that of the thousands of dark beings who appeared to have agreed among themselves to move at one uniform rate.

In the course of my progress, my thoughts returned to the house that I had left. In this unusual city where all the houses have three stories and identical frontages, where everything is distant from everything else, which way should I turn? Through what street could I retrace my steps? I had not the slightest idea. Furthermore, even if I did regain the right street, I felt that I would be unable to recognize the house in which I was to reside henceforward. When I saw it yesterday, it loomed up in the dark and seemed as somber as the evening air.

Lost in my melancholy musings, I was pushed by

groups of tall people and went across two or three avenues without having intended to do so. Whenever I crossed one of them, I felt I was turning my back towards the gloomy looking house which I had visited the previous evening. Then, lost in this crowd, which was so dense that my eyes were hurting, I experienced a feeling of what I can only call solitude. In the end, I reached a gentle slope. I saw it was a place where five or six streets converged. The flood of humanity, which up to now had been moving in the same direction, found itself swollen when it reached the bottom of the slope by waves coming towards it from every direction, and creating a gentle swirl.

At the foot of the slope, there was an ash-colored marble statue of a lion. The tail was quite thin, but the head, merging into the mane and creating an eddy-like configuration, was the size of an enormous barrel. With its front paws stretched out before it, the beast rested in the middle of the constantly arriving and receding crowd. In actual fact, there were two lions. The ground below them was paved. A great bronze column dominated the square. Lost in this silently surging sea of humanity, I raised my eyes towards the top of the column. It stretched upwards as far as my eyes could follow it. Above it was the immense and all-enveloping sky. The lofty column seemed to split the sky in two. I could not see what was right on the top. Once again, under the pressure of the crowd, I unwillingly rushed through the square and found myself in a street to the right. Later on, I turned round and saw a tiny silhouette[21] rising above the column, now as thin as a pole.

[21] Horatio Nelson (1758–1805), whose statue dominates Trafalgar Square. The column, fifty meters in height, was erected in 1842. The four lions were added twenty-five years later.

11
The Human Being

Had O-Saku got up too early? At all events, she was rushing about everywhere and saying, "Hasn't the hairdresser come yet? She's still not here!" She was sure, however, that yesterday evening she had asked her to come. She had reached the stage of being unable to sleep peacefully until she had heard her reply, "I have no other clients, and I will arrange to be here at nine o'clock without fail." The clock now showed that there were only five minutes left before it struck nine. As O-Saku looked annoyed, the servant went out to see what was happening. Standing before her mirror, which she had placed in front of a *shōji,* O-Saku leaned slightly forwards in order to see herself clearly. She opened her mouth wide, exposing two rows of faultlessly aligned white teeth. At this moment, there were nine knocks on the door. She straightened up immediately and, sliding open the *fusuma* of the next room, said, "What are you doing? Do you know it's past nine o'clock? You'll make us late if you don't get up!" On realizing the time, O-Saku's protector had just sat up in bed. As soon as he saw her through the half-open door, he added, "I'm getting up, you see!" and briskly did so.

O-Saku was already coming back from the kitchen with a toothpick, some toothpaste and soap and a towel, and she held out all of these to the man, saying, "Come on—hurry up!"

"I am going to have a shave when I come back from the bath," he told her, going down to the front door to put on his shoes. The hem of his cotton kimono could be seen below the garment of coarse

silk which he had put on over it. "Just a moment or
two—I'll be right back!" and O-Saku once again disappeared, running to the back of the house. While
waiting for her to come back, he had begun to use the
toothpick. O-Saku opened the drawer of a little chest
of drawers, took out an envelope in which she put a
coin, and came back to him. As he was busy with the
toothpick, the man merely took the little envelope
from O-Saku without a word. He slid back the open-
work door and stepped outside. O-Saku's eyes briefly
followed him, also observing the line of his shoulders
and an end of the towel still showing and swinging at
each step he took. But she promptly went back into
the house, sat down in front of her dressing table,
and looked at herself again. She then half opened one
of the drawers and slightly bent her head. A moment
later, she took two or three objects out of the drawer, put them on the *tatami* and examined them carefully. She kept only one of the three things she had
troubled to take out, carefully replacing the other
two in the drawer. She opened a second drawer, her
expression once more becoming thoughtful. O-Saku
thus spent at least half an hour sorting the contents,
devoting a lot of thought to them and then replacing
them. The whole of the time, she kept anxiously looking at the clock. When she had at last finished match-
ing her trinkets, she packed everything into a large
square piece of yellow fabric that she then deposited
in a corner of the room. At this same moment, the
hairdresser arrived, entering through the service
door and speaking loudly as if she herself could not
believe she had managed to come. "I am so very
sorry to be late!" Audibly out of breath, she proffered
some excuse.

"It is I who must apologize for having sent for you

when you are so busy!" said O-Saku, offering her a long thin pipe and inviting her to have a smoke.

As she had come without her assistant, it took her some considerable time to do O-Saku's hair. By now the man had returned from the bathroom, after his shave. O-Saku had told the hairdresser that her patron was taking her to the Yūrakuza,[22] and she had invited Mii-chan to join them. "What a piece of luck for you! I would go with you myself if only I had the chance!" the hairdresser joked, in order to make pleasant conversation. She then left, wishing them an enjoyable day.

The man had slightly raised the square of yellow fabric. "This is what you are thinking of wearing?" he asked. "I think what you were wearing the other day suits you better!"

"But that's what I wore when I went to see Mii-chan at the end of last year!"

"Oh, really? Well you're right, and as for me, should I wear my cotton wool-lined *haori*? It seems to be rather cold...?"

"Oh no—what an idea! Don't even think of such a thing! What impression would you make? You're always wearing the same things!"—and the lined overcoat with *kasuri*[23] motifs remained in a drawer.

When she had finished making up, she donned a fashionable coat of machine-stitched silk and wound a fur round her neck, and very soon the two of them

[22] The first theater in the Western style. It was built in 1908 and destroyed in the great earthquake of Tokyo and the surrounding district in 1923.
[23] A term which may be applied to the fabric itself, generally cotton, or to the design, the most usual being a kind of little square of which the ends extend in a similar way to the shapes on a partition.

were on their way. In the street, she was almost
hanging on his arm while talking to him. When they
reached a crossing, their attention was attracted by
a crowd in front of the police station. O-Saku,
supporting herself by holding the folds of the man's
cape, stood on tiptoe to try to peer through the
crowd and see what was happening.

In the very middle of the crowd, a man came
staggering along. He wore a tunic with the name of
the outfitters on the back and could neither remain
upright nor sit down properly. He must have fallen
down in the mud a number of times, judging by the
faded color of his wet garment. The policeman asked
him, "What are you talking about?" In a thick voice
and with a swanky air, he replied, "I'm a human
being!" Each time, the crowd burst out laughing.
O-Saku laughed, too, looking at her companion.
The drunk grew angry. Rolling his ferocious eyes,
he looked all about him and said, "Wha-wha-what
are you laughing at? Yes, I'm a man—a human being!
What's funny about that? Perhaps I don't look up
to much, but…." His chin sank towards his chest.
But a second later, as if everything was returning
to his memory, he started yelling again, "I'm a
human being!"

While this was going on, a big, robust-looking
fellow with a sunburnt face, wearing the same tunic
and pulling a cart, appeared out of the blue. Turning
to the drunk, he said, "Get into the cart, you silly
idiot! I'll take you back!" A smile lit up the tipsy man's
face as he expressed hearty thanks. He hoisted himself into the cart and stretched out on his back. He
blinked two or three times, his eyelids hiding the
melancholy glance that he directed towards the sky.
Then he burst out, "Crowd of riff-raff! Perhaps I don't

look up to much, but I'm a human being!"

"Yes, of course you're a human being. It's just that you must be reasonable!" and the big fellow tied him up with a cord. He then made off, jogging along the street with the cart, and the drunk allowed himself to be taken away like a pig with its throat cut. Still holding on to the tails of her companion's cape, O-Saku followed the disappearing cart with her eyes. It went further and further away, finally vanishing amid the New Year decorations over the entrances to the houses. While proceeding towards Mii-chan's house, she delightedly thought she would have yet another incident to relate.

12
The Pheasant

I had a few visitors, and we were all sitting around the brazier and talking when, all of sudden, in came a young stranger. I had never heard his name or met him before—he was completely unknown to me. He brought no letter of introduction and simply asked, when the front door had been opened, to be allowed to come in. He appeared in front of the assembled company in the drawing room holding out a pheasant. After the customary greetings, he deposited the bird in the middle of the room, saying that he had received it from his native country and would like us to accept it as a gift.

It was a cold day. We all enjoyed the pheasant, cooked in a pot. When the time came to prepare it, the young man, wearing a pair of *hakama*,[24] installed himself in the kitchen, plucked the pheasant himself, cut it up, and divided up the portions. He had a long, narrow face and wore very thick glasses beneath a pale forehead. But what struck me more than his shortsightedness or his brown moustache was his *hakama*. It was made of very gaudy *kokura*[25] silk, with wide stripes, such as an ordinary student could not possibly have worn. With his hands resting flat on his *hakama*, he explained that he was from the Morioka region.

A week later, the young man came again. This time he brought a manuscript. The quality of the text left much to be desired, and I told him quite frankly what I thought of it. He took his departure, saying that he

[24] Wide trousers worn over a kimono.
[25] Duck cloth woven at Kokura in the northern part of Kūyshū Island.

would rewrite it. About a week later, he returned with some sheets held in the top of his kimono. Every time he called, he never failed to hand over, before taking his leave, a few pages he had written. On one occasion, he even brought a very lengthy work that filled three volumes. But this was the worst he had ever written. Once or twice I offered to a magazine what seemed to be the best of the lot. But it could only be due to an editor's benevolence that it was published, and it seems that he did not receive a penny for it. It was on that occasion that I learned of the difficulties with which he was having to cope. He said that from then onwards, he intended to live by his pen.

One day, he brought me something very curious. It consisted of dried chrysanthemums, the petals of which had been superimposed one by one after having been hardened with a kind of fine paste. He explained that it replaced, for Buddhists who abstained from fish, the tiny, lace-thin dried sardines. The companion who accompanied him eagerly performed the task of scalding the vegetables, and we took some saké to accompany this dish. Another time he brought me a sprig of artificial lily-of-the-valley. He explained that it had been made by his sister, and wound the wire forming the "branch" around his fingers. I then learned for the first time that he lived with his younger sister. They rented a room on the first floor of the house of a timber merchant, and she went to a daily embroidery lesson. On his next visit, he had a sheet of newspaper from which he extracted an ash beige collar of which the knot was ornamented with a white embroidered butterfly. He offered to leave it for me if I had use for it. Yasuno asked me to give it to him and went off with the knot.

The young man returned from time to time. He never failed to tell me of the scenery of his native region, its customs, legends and traditional ceremonies. He told me his father had been a learned man where Chinese characters were concerned. He added that he was very skilful in the engraving of seals. His grandmother had been in the service of a *daimyo*.[26] She had won the favor of the lord and, as she had been born in the year of the ape, he had presented her from time to time with some object associated with that animal. Among other things, he had given her a picture of an ape with long arms by Kazan.[27] He promised to bring it with him to show me on his next visit. And then he stopped coming.

Spring gave way to summer. I was starting to forget the young man. But one day, when the heat was so intense that I found it difficult to read and was seated motionless in the center of the living room in a spot sheltered from the sunlight, wearing nothing but an unlined kimono, he arrived unexpectedly.

He was wearing his gaudy *hakama* as usual, and was carefully wiping away the perspiration which kept forming on his pale forehead. He struck me as having grown a little thinner. After some considerable hesitation, he finally asked me to lend him twenty yen. He intended to be quite open about it. A friend of his had been taken ill and he had at once had him admitted to hospital. But money was required for the most immediate problems. He had asked here, there and everywhere, but in vain. Finally, he had decided to knock on my door. Such was his explanation.

[26] A feudal lord.
[27] Watanabe Kazan (1784–1841), a painter and writer well qualified in the European sciences.

I paused in my reading and observed him. As always, he was sitting in an extremely correct manner, his hands resting flat on his thighs. In a subdued voice, he said, "Please!"

"Is your friend's family so lacking in means?" I asked.

No, that was not the problem, but they lived a long way away and could not help in an emergency, which was why he had come to me. The money was expected to arrive from his native region in two weeks' time, and he would repay me immediately. I acceded to his request. He then unwrapped a *kakemono*,[28] explaining that it was by Kazan and that he had once mentioned it to me. He unfolded it in front of me. It was a fairly large picture. I did not form any clear idea of the quality of the work. I consulted a list of seals, but I did not see how the painting, the signature or the seal resembled those of Watanabe Kazan or Yokoyama Kazan.[29]

As the young man made to leave, I tried to refuse it, assuring him that it was not worth troubling about, but he was already hurrying out of the house. On the following day, he came back for the money. After that, I heard nothing further from him. The two weeks, at the end of which he had promised to repay me, went by without any sign of him. I concluded that he had taken advantage of me. The *kakemono,* depicting an ape, was hanging on the wall. Autumn came. I had put on a lined garment and—full of resolution—had firmly decided to set to work, when Nagatsuka arrived once again in order to borrow money from me. I was extremely annoyed at having to continue lending money.

[28] A hanging picture scroll.
[29] Yokoyama Kazan (1784–1837), a painter and native of Kyoto.

Suddenly remembering the young man, I told Nagatsuka that if he would care to go and recover the money which I had lent, he could then have the loan he needed. He scratched his head and hesitated. After a moment or two, he agreed to take this step. I wrote out a request to hand the bearer of the letter the money which I had lent, attached the drawing of the ape and handed everything over to Nagatsuka.

The next day, Nagatsuka returned in a carriage. He hastily took a letter out of the top of his kimono and handed it to me, and I saw at once that it was my own letter of the day before. It had not been opened. I then asked him why he had not called on the young man. A frown appeared on his forehead, and he confessed that, although he had gone there, he had not felt capable of delivering the message as their circumstances were so tragic. "The accommodation was dirty, the wife was at work sewing and he himself was ill … it really wasn't the right time to call with a claim for money, and I told them they need not worry. I calmed him down and simply handed over the painting before taking my departure."

"So there you are!" I could only express my astonishment by a murmured "Oh well!"

The next day I received a card from the young man. He had duly received the *kakemono* and apologized for having lied to me. I put the card among other papers in a basket, and once again forgot all about him.

Then winter returned, and, as usual, I had a hectic New Year's Day. While I was taking advantage of an interval between two visits to get some work done, the servant arrived with a packet in oiled paper. It was round and made a dull sound when tapped. The sender was the young man who had faded from my memory. I opened it up and found, wrapped in newspaper, a golden pheasant. It was accompanied by a letter. This said, "Owing to various circumstances, I have had to return to my native province. I expect to be able to return the money which you were kind enough to lend me when I am in the capital about March." The paper, hardened by the bird's blood, was not easy to unstick.

It was a Thursday,[30] of all days, so a few young men were due to spend the evening at the house. Seated around a large table we consumed the pheasant simmering in a pot. And I sincerely wished good luck to the pale young man in the gaudy *kokura* silk *hakama*. After my visitors had taken their departure, I wrote him a few words of thanks. And I added that he need no longer worry about the money I had lent him the year before.

[30] A reference to the *Mokuyō-kai* ("Thursday Group") regularly held at Sōseki's house from October 1906 onwards.

13
Mona Lisa

When Sunday comes, Ibuka, wearing a scarf round his neck and with his hands tucked into the sleeves of his kimono, drops into the second-hand shops along the way to rummage through their contents. He fixes on the dirtiest of all, the one that gives the impression of offering anything the preceding generation may have thrown out, and the objects on which he chances to light are turned over and over in his hands. He has never been qualified in this sphere, and cannot even hazard a guess as to the quality of what he sees, but by picking out unusual and inexpensive articles, he tells himself that once a year at the very least he manages to unearth a real "find".

Last month Ibuka bought the cover of a cast-iron kettle for fifteen sen and he now uses it as a paperweight. The other Sunday, for the sum of twenty-five sen, he acquired a bronze sword hilt, and from this too he made a paperweight. Today he seems to have decided to obtain something larger. A *kakemono*, a picture or a calligraphic production—in short, something that will be noticed immediately—is what he requires as an ornament for his study. While examining the objects in one of the shops, he discovers a portrait, in color, of a Western woman. It is covered with dust and has been left facing the wall. On the worn pulley over a well, there is an indescribable vase from which extends the yellowed mouthpiece of a wooden flute, hiding part of the picture.

The Western painting does not fit in with all this bric-à-brac, but its tints transcend its period. Blackened by the passage of time, it seems made to be found in this shop rather than in any other. Ibuka immediately values it at a low figure and is disconcerted to find that the price is one yen. But the glass is unbroken and the frame looks robust, so he persuades the old dealer to let him have it for eighty sen.

When Ibuka returns to his house carrying the portrait of a woman under his arm, the cold day is drawing to a close. He enters his study, which is plunged in darkness. He hastens to unpack his acquisition, places the picture against the wall and seats himself in front of it. While he is absorbed in contemplation of the portrait, his wife enters with the lamp. Ibuka asks her to bring the light closer to the picture, and once again examines every detail of this framed portrait which he has acquired for eighty sen. The picture as a whole is dark and colorless; only the woman's face has a yellowish tint. This, too, is doubtless due to the period in which the picture was painted. Without getting up, Ibuka turns to his wife and asks her what she thinks of the picture. She lifts the lamp a little higher and gazes silently at the woman's yellowed complexion. After a moment, she says, "This disturbs me!" Ibuka simply laughs and tells her it cost just eighty sen.

After dinner he takes a little stool, drives a nail into the sculpted surface of the border above the *fusuma* and hangs up his new purchase. His wife does her best to dissuade him, declaring that there is no knowing what might happen with this woman there. She feels ill at ease looking at it and it would be better not to hang it up, but Ibuka replies, "You're too highly strung!" and has his own way.

His wife goes back into the *cha-no-ma*. Ibuka sits down in his study and starts to compile his notes.

After ten minutes he suddenly raises his head, with a desire to look at the portrait. He puts down his pen and directs his gaze from left to right and then from right to left. The yellowed woman then gave a faint smile in her frame. Ibuka does not take his eyes off her mouth. It is due to the interplay achieved by the painter between light and shadow. The corners of the thin lips rise in such a way as to create an almost invisible dimple. One could almost imagine that the mouth, hitherto shut, is about to open. Or that the lips, up to that moment partly open, have been closed on purpose. There is no apparent reason. Ibuka feels slightly disturbed, but once again begins to concentrate on his work.

As far as his notes are concerned, half the work consists of a transcription which does not require a great deal of attention, so that after a minute or two he once again raises his head and looks at the painting. The mouth is certainly concealing something. The face itself reflects considerable calm. The stretched eyelids are raised and the pupils view the room with an air of serenity. Ibuka once again returns to his work.

That evening Ibuka looks at the portrait a number of times. And he begins to think that his wife is not so far wrong. The next day, however, without revealing any of his thoughts to his wife, he goes off to his work at the town hall. When he returns at about four, he finds yesterday's picture laid upside down on his table. His wife tells him that shortly after midday the frame fell on the floor. Needless to say, the glass was smashed into smithereens. Ibuka turns the picture over. The hooks through which he had placed the string have come off, for which he can find no explanation. Ibuka takes this opportunity to open up the frame. He finds a Western periodical folded in four and laid flat against the portrait. He opens it and reads an article which describes strange and gloomy things: "Mona Lisa's mouth conceals the eternal essence of the feminine heart. Leonardo da Vinci is the only artist since civilization began to have succeeded in painting this enigma. To this day nobody has succeeded in penetrating the secret."

The following day, Ibuka goes to the town hall and asks everybody who Mona Lisa was. Nobody knows. "Well then, who is Leonardo da Vinci?" No one has any idea. Deferring to his wife's views, Ibuka sells this picture, from which no good can come, to a ragman for five sen.

14
The Fire

Out of breath, I stopped and looked up. Sparks were already flying over me. In the depths of the clear and frosty sky, flakes of fire were fluttering about, flying off and immediately vanishing. Just when they seemed to have disappeared, they were replaced by more from all sides, each looking brighter than the last, covering the immensity of the sky and flitting about in all directions. Then, just as quickly, they disappeared. When I looked along the path of their flight, they seemed to have combined gigantic fountains at one and the same source and colored the entire surface of the frozen sky without leaving the tiniest interstice. A few meters away, there was a big temple amid long stone steps. A thick fir tree serenely extended its branches in the evening air and rose from the embankment to its full height. The flames leaped behind it. Only the black trunk and the motionless branches were spared, all the rest was scarlet. The fire had without doubt spread above the embankment. Some two hundred meters up the side, on the left, the center could no doubt be reached.

I started walking again, this time more quickly. I was overtaken by people behind me. Some called out to those who passed them. The dark street had come alive of its own accord. I continued as far as the bottom of the slope, and now that I wanted to go up again, it was so steep that I grew out of breath. From end to end, heads could be seen and cries heard from all around. Above the ascending road, the flames swirled around ceaselessly. I felt as if I was going to burn before I had had a chance to turn around and go back if I became engulfed by this human eddy that threatened to force me right up to the top.

About a hundred meters further on, there was a long street that wound upwards to the left. Believing that this would be the easiest and safest route to the top, I changed my mind and, struggling through the crowd, I was about to reach the turning when the fire engine, with its ear-splitting siren, arrived from the other side. It was advancing at breathtaking speed, almost threatening to kill anything that did not give way, and with the deafening sound of their hooves the horses, their nostrils steaming, continued their upward rush. Frothing at the mouth and neck, they pointed their ears forward, came to a stop and then suddenly bounded forwards with astonishing vigor. At the same time, the breast of each horse, when it brushed against a man in a tunic, gleamed like soft velvet. The wide vermilion-painted wheels of the fire engine were rotating dangerously near my legs, almost touching them. By now, however, the pump was being hoisted straight to the top.

Reaching the middle of the slope, I noticed that the flames which until then had been dancing in front of me were now behind me, contrary to what I had expected. Once at the top, I would have to turn left once more if I wanted to go back. To one side I discovered a little alleyway. When I, in turn, was pushed into it by the people surrounding me I found it was extremely crowded. Not even the smallest space was left between any two people. Shouts were heard. There was no doubt that the fire was raging on the other side.

After ten minutes, I was at last able to leave the alley and get back to the street. The latter was no wider than a corporation building[31] at most, and it was already full of people. Hardly had I emerged from the narrow passage than I saw, stationary in front of me, the fire engine which only a short while before had been tearing up the ground in order to reach the top. The horses had successfully brought it this far, but a few meters farther on had met with the impassable obstacle presented by the turning. It was helpless before the conflagration. Then flames danced before my eyes.

The people who had been pushed against me were asking again and again, "Where is it? Where is it?" Those to whom the question was addressed invariably replied, "It's there! Over there!" But none of them could reach the place. The flames were becoming ever more intense and menacingly rose to the calm sky as if intending to carry it away.

The next day, taking advantage of an early afternoon walk to satisfy my curiosity as to the seat of the fire, I ascended the slope, crossed the same alleyway as the day before, and found myself in front of the corporation building where the fire engine had come to a halt. I followed the turning a few meters farther on and began to walk at a casual pace in search of the place in question but could find nothing but houses in neat rows, their canopies touching and looking as if they had been drawn back for the winter. Nowhere could I find any trace of a fire. At the point where I thought it had broken out, all I could see was a succession of pretty hedges, from one of which the almost imperceptible sound of *koto* reached my ears.

---

[31] In Japanese, *kumiyashiki*, a building like a *nagaya* for lower officials who formed a kind of corporation.

15
Fog

All last night I heard a kind of crackling overhead. This was because there was a big station close by—Clapham Junction. This station is a meeting point for over a thousand trains every day. A rough calculation shows that on average a train arrives or departs every minute. In thick fog, every locomotive, I do not know by what means, emits a signal which sounds like a rocket a few seconds before entering the station. It must be realized that at such times visual signals are of no use at all, both the green and red signals being completely obscured.

I jumped out of bed, lifted the curtain over the window facing north and looked out at the street. The whole scene was blurred. Nothing could be seen down below, from the patch of grass to the red brick outer wall about two meters high surrounding the house on three sides. The garden contained nothing but useless ornaments. Motionless and melancholy, everything seemed to be set in ice. The neighboring garden looked just the same. It had a pleasant lawn, and when the warm spring arrived, a white-bearded old man went out there to enjoy the sun. He always had a parrot with him perched on his right arm, and he put his face so close to its beak that it looked as if he was about to be pecked. The parrot beat his wings and squawked incessantly. When the old man did not appear, a young girl, hitching up the hem of her long dress, constantly ran a lawn mower over the grass. This garden, still so clear in my memory, was now swallowed up by the fog, and there was nothing to distinguish it from the boarding house where I was staying, disused and deserted, with the houses all in one unbroken line.

On the other side of the street, which passed the back of the house, could be seen the slender towers of a church built in the Gothic style. At the top of the gray towers, pointed skywards, the bells pealed out. On Sundays, in particular, it was intolerable. On this occasion, it was not only the slender pointed steeple that was hidden from view. Not even the edifice itself, with its uneven flagstones, could be discerned. However, I then thought I could make out a vague black shape, although there was no ringing to be heard. The sound was imprisoned in the deep, dense shadow of the bells, even the contours of which could not be distinguished.

In the street, one could not see more than four meters ahead. Once this space had been crossed, there was another of the same length ahead. You could imagine that the world was reduced to a square of four meters: the farther you went, the more squares of this kind you discovered. On the other hand, the world from which you had just come belonged to the past and was erased at every fresh step.

While I was waiting for the bus at the corner of the street, I suddenly noticed, in the gray air, the head of a horse. But the passengers on the double-decker had not yet emerged from the fog. I walked through the fog and jumped into the vehicle, then looked down and found that the horse's head had become blurred, and was now nothing more than a vague contour. Two buses met and passed. This was a pleasant moment, I told myself, watching them move further and further apart. While I thus mused, objects receded into the impenetrable space.

Everything disappeared into an infinite colorless universe. I was able to make out two pale shapes fluttering about on Westminster Bridge. I concentrated my gaze on what turned out to be two gulls lightly hovering in the air like a vision in a dream. At that moment, Big Ben, high above my head, solemnly struck ten.

As I had finished what I had to do at Victoria Station, I walked along the section of the river which passes close to the Tate Gallery and arrived at Battersea. The dark gray surroundings I had seen until then suddenly vanished. I found myself encircled. A thick heavy fog passed around my eyes, lips and nostrils as if liquid coal was being poured on to me. My overcoat was so damp so that it seemed to be stuck to my skin. I found it difficult to breathe, just as if I had been taking little sips of an arrowroot infusion. As for my feet, they felt as if they were treading the floor of a cave.

Plunged into this depressing grayness, I remained for a moment in a state of semi-torpor. I certainly did have the impression of a constant stream of passersby. But unless their shoulders actually brushed against mine, how could I help doubting their reality? At this moment, a tiny dot in the ocean fog, some yellow object hardly bigger than a beam, moved with a wavy motion, giving out a pale light. I took a few steps towards it. A face then made its appearance behind the glass front of a shop. Somebody had lit a lamp. The interior of the shop was comparatively light. The occupants were moving about in a normal manner. At last I felt reassured.

Having passed through Battersea, I felt my way along towards the little hill on the opposite side. But I discovered nothing except houses. There were rows of streets all similar to one another. No doubt you could easily lose your way there, even in fine weather. I think I had taken the second turning to the left. It then seemed as if I had covered about four hundred meters in the same direction. After this, nothing was clear to me. Alone in the dark street, I listened carefully. From the right approaching footsteps could be heard. But when they had come to within about ten meters of me, they came to a stop, then gradually receded. In the end, I no longer heard anything. All fell silent. Once more alone in the dark, I had not the slightest idea how I was going to find my way back to my boarding house.

William James Craig (1834–1906), a Shakespeare scholar who gave private tuition to Sōseki for ten months.* "His face is extremely original. As a European, he has a high nose with a pronounced bridge which, because of its thickness, looks like mine, a nose which does not evoke a pleasant, cheerful impression." ("Craig Sensei", p. 112)

Craig's House at 55a, Gloucester Place, London W1, where he lived with his maid Jane. "Like a swallow, my teacher Mr Craig has his nest on the fourth floor. If one looks up from the street, it is impossible to see his window." ("Craig Sensei", p. 110)

All photographs courtesy of the Sōseki Museum.

Sarah Waller	Wife	m	42	
Marjorie do	daughter		15	Hopeful Teacher
Kate do	do		14	
Harديست Brett	Head	m 25		Ironmonger fit
Sarah do	Wife	m	40	
Catherine Sparrow	Sister	S	36	
K. Natsume	Boarder	m 34		Instructor of Letter
Isabel Roberts	do	S 18		
Kotaro Tanakki	do	m 29		General (14)
Annie Perin	Servant	S	23	
Alfred E. Oddy	Head	S 26		Surgeon
Harold E.C. do	Brother	S	21	
Elsie M. Hoddwitt	Visitor	S	23	
Gladys m. Street	do	S	15	
Total of Males and of Females..			**12 16**	

Detail from the 1901 Census. K. Natsume (Kinnosuke was his real name) is listed in this Census, as was another Japanese border, Tanaka Kōtaro,[†] who lived at the same address.

THOMAS TILLING HORSE BUS
Clapham Junction – Tooting – Wimbledon – Raynes Park 1900

A horse-drawn bus, typical of those operating in London around 1900. In his early days in London, Sōseki was unable to use the London bus service because he could not determine which route to take.

[†] *Japanese names follow the Japanese convention, that is, with the family name first.*

The first blue "English Heritage" plaque commemorating a Japanese celebrity was unveiled at 81 The Chase, South London, on 22 March 2002, by Professor Yōko Matsuoka McClain, Sōseki's granddaughter, and HE Orita Masaki, Japanese Ambassador to Britain.

BOARD (PARTIAL) RESIDENCE REQUIRED, by City gentleman, W.C. district.—Address A. A., care of J. W. Vickers, 5, Nicholas-lane, E.C.

BOARD and RESIDENCE WANTED, for nurse and baby (1½ months). Country or seaside.—State terms (which must be moderate) to Mrs. Baker, 123, West-end-lane, Hampstead, London, N.W.

BOARD RESIDENCE WANTED, by a Japanese gentleman, in a strictly private English family, with literary taste. Quiet and convenient quarters in N., N.W., or S.W. preferred.—Address Z. V., care of Barker, 2, Castle-court, Birchin-lane, E.C.

CITY MAN wants BOARD-RESIDENCE, with superior social family (English or French). Young society.—Full particulars to M. 974, Messrs. Deacon's, Leadenhall-street, E.C.

FARMHOUSE APARTMENTS or FURNISHED COUNTRY HOUSE (five bed rooms) WANTED, with whole or part attendance, for August and part September, within 30 miles of London. Good garden and tennis lawn indispensable.—Address, stating terms, Farm, Box 4,270, Postal Department, Daily Telegraph, Fleet-street, E.C.

FARMHOUSE APARTMENTS REQUIRED, for month of August, for family. Shady garden. Pretty country. Mo-

This advertisement, which Sōseki inserted in the *Daily Telegraph* on 11 July 1901, led to his final and favorite lodgings in Britain, 81 The Chase.

Group photograph taken at 81 The Chase in 1903. *Back*: Priscilla and Elizabeth Leale, who ran the boarding house; *left*: unknown; *right*: Masuda Takashi, founder of Mitsui & Co., one of Japan's largest trading companies; *front*: Shimomura Kanzan, the famous Japanese artist who stayed at the boarding house after Sōseki had left.

81, The Chase, Clapham Common, London SW4, where Sōseki lived from 20 July 1901 to 4 December 1902.

Lavender Hill, where Sōseki practiced riding his bicycle, a pastime recommended by his landladies Priscilla and Elizabeth Leale who were concerned that he kept too much to his room.

The Pavement, Clapham Common, SW4, c. 1899. Sōseki would walk home to 81 The Chase from the nearby Underground station.

Carlyle House,
24 Cheyne Row, Chelsea
SW3, former home
of Thomas Carlyle,
Scottish historian,
critic and philosopher,
which Sōseki visited
with Dr Ikeda Kikunae
(inventor of the
artificial seasoning
Ajinomoto) on 3 August
1901. Their names can
still be seen in the
Visitor's Book.

Mrs Strong, Curator of Carlyle House at
the time Soseki and Ikeda visited it on
3 August 1901.

John Henry Dixon, FSA (1838–1926), a notable Pitlochry personality, who founded the Scottish Boy Scouts in 1908. He had many and varied interests, including political and philanthropic work in the town. A Fellow of the Antiquarian Society, he studied history and folklore and also had an avid interest in Japanese art and culture. He published *Pitlochry: Past and Present* in 1925.

Dixon's former house, currently the Dandarach Hotel, where Sōseki stayed for about ten days in October 1902.

The Japanese garden at Dixon's house in Pitlochry. *From left*: John Henry Dixon, O. Mackenzie and a Japanese guest.

16
The Kakemono

Old Daitō had sworn to erect a slab over his wife's grave before the third anniversary of her death. Having to rely on the limited resources of his son, he found that the days had passed and spring had arrived before he had saved even the tiniest sum. "When I think it will soon be March 8th, the anniversary of your mother's death!" he said to his son, giving him a reproachful look, his son simply replied, "Dear, dear! Yes, that's true...." Finally, old Daitō decided to raise the necessary money by selling a picture to which he was very attached and which his family had owned for generations.

When he told his son what he had in mind, hoping to hear his opinion, the latter raised not the slightest objection, which caused him some resentment. His son worked in the Sacred Buildings Bureau of the Ministry of the Interior for a monthly salary of forty yen. As his wife not only had to care for their two children but also show filial devotion by looking after old Daitō, she suffered much fatigue. If it had not been for the old man, the precious painting would long ago have been converted into things of more practical use.

This *kakemono* was a painting on silk, about thirty centimeters wide, and somewhat brownish with age. When it hung on the wall in the living room, in which there was not much light, it was impossible to make out what it represented, as the painting itself was dark. The old man maintained that the mauve flower in the painting was the work of Ōjakushi.[32]

[32] Chinese artist (1279–1368), who specialized in drawing flowers and birds.

Once or twice a month he took it out of a little cupboard with shelves, dusted the box of paulownia wood, extracted the roll of silk with the greatest care, and feverishly attached it to the wall of the alcove, which hardly measured a meter. He then settled down to study it in comfort. Once the eye had become accustomed to it, a motif similar to a large spot of tainted blood was seen to emerge from the brownish background. This still left a few almost imperceptible places where the presence of subsequently obliterated verdigris might be supposed. Looking at this red Chinese painting of uncertain origin, he would completely forget the things of this world in which he was sufficiently experienced to begin to wonder whether he had not lived too long. On certain days he looked at the picture while smoking, or drinking a cup of tea. Otherwise he was content just to examine it.

"Grandfather, tell us, what is it?" the children would ask, pointing at the picture. Coming back to earth as if once again conscious of time, the old man would slowly rise to his feet and set about rolling up the *kakemono*, advising the children not to touch it. Then the children would say, "Grandpa, what about the sugared almonds?" "Yes," he would reply. "I'll go and get you some, but don't get up to mischief while I'm gone!" And he would finish rolling up the *kakemono*, replacing it in its paulownia wood box, which in turn was put back in the little cupboard. Then he would go out for a walk. Before coming back, he went to the local confectioners and bought two packets of peppermint flavored sugared almonds, which he handed to the children, saying, "Here are your sweets!" His son had married late, and the children were six and four.

The day after he had discussed the matter with his son, the old man went out early in the morning, carrying the paulownia wood box wrapped in a piece of square fabric. Towards four o'clock in the afternoon, he came home with the box still in his hands. The children rushed into the hall shouting, "Have you got the sugared almonds, Grandpa?" But the old man, without saying a word, went towards the living room, took the *kakemono* out of its box, hung it on the wall and gazed at it in dreamy contemplation. He had visited forty-five second-hand dealers, but apparently nobody had thought as much of the *kakemono* as the old man had hoped, some saying that it did not bear the artist's seal and others saying that the paint had flaked off.

His son said a second-hand shop was not the right place to try. The old man agreed with him, adding that those dealers had no knowledge of such things. About a fortnight later, he went out once more with the paulownia wood box under his arm. Armed with a recommendation, he went and showed the picture to a friend of the head of the department where his son was employed. Once again, he returned without bringing any sugared almonds. As soon as his son came home, he rushed to tell him that he would never let the *kakemono* pass into the hands of someone so completely ignorant of such things and who only had imitation ones, practically implying that his son was unethical in his dealings.

During the first few days of February, an acceptable purchaser turned up by chance, and the old man let the art lover have the drawing. He then immediately went to Yanaka,[33] where he ordered a magnificent gravestone for his late wife. The amount left over was placed in a postal account. About five days later, he went out for his customary walk, but he returned some two hours sooner than usual. He carried a big bag of sweets in each hand.

The *kakemono* which he had sold to a certain collector still being still on his mind, he had asked to see it. He found it had been hung up without any attempt at elegance in a little room measuring four and a half *tatami* and used for taking tea. In front of the picture there was a vase containing an almost transparent wax-colored branch from a plum tree. He said he had been offered tea in this room. The old man said his mind was more at ease now that the picture was no longer in his possession. His son agreed. And for three whole days the children stuffed themselves with sugared almonds.

[33] A district of Tokyo, not far from Ueno, in what is now the Taitō area. The enormous cemetery is also a place for walks and is particularly popular when the cherry trees are in bloom.

17
The 11th of February

It was a room that opened to the south. With their backs to the light, there were about thirty children leaning over their slates with their dark heads all in a neat row, when the teacher came into the classroom from the corridor. He was short and lean, with big eyes and a beard covering his face from chin to cheek, which made him look older than he was. In addition, the collar of his kimono, touching his rough chin, had a dubious appearance; it seemed to bear traces of stains. By reason of this beard, which he let grow without tending it, and also because he had never been heard to scold his pupils, nobody took the schoolmaster seriously.

He immediately took a piece of chalk and wrote *Kigen setsu*[34] in big letters on the blackboard. The pupils all bent over their desks, their heads almost touching them, and began to write. Drawing himself up to his modest height, the teacher cast his eye around the whole class, then left it soon afterwards and walked along the corridor.

A pupil halfway along the third row then rose from his seat, went and stood by the teacher's desk, picked up the chalk which the teacher had just used, added a stroke to the *ki* of *Kigen setsu* and added a

---

[34] Commemorating the accession of the Emperor Jimmu, the chronological starting point for the eras in Japan. Originally corresponding to the first day of the year according to the old calendar (29th January), the date formally adopted in 1873 was 11th February, which became a public holiday.

further character.[35] His classmates looked on in astonishment, without laughing. He then returned to his seat, but had hardly sat down again before the teacher reappeared. The blackboard immediately attracted the teacher's attention.

"I see someone has corrected my *ki* and replaced it by another, which is not wrong, by the way, but the first was correct too!" he said, glancing around the classroom. Nobody moved a muscle.

I myself was the pupil who had corrected the teacher's *kanji*. To this day, in the year 42 of Meiji,[36] I cannot help still feeling ashamed of this petty trick, and every time I think of it I regret it was the principal, of whom we were all afraid, rather than Mr Fukuda, who seemed to have aged before his time.

---

[35] Between 1906 and 1907, a debate started as to the choice between two idiograms for the *ki* of *Kigen*. The *ki* used by the schoolmaster in Sōseki's memoirs is that in the *Kojiki* ("Chronicle of Older Things"), compiled by imperial command, completed in 712 and rich in narrative and myths. The other is the *ki* of *Nihon Shoki* ("Annals of Japan"), a chronicle compiled in 720, introducing variants into mythology and having a diplomatic dimension in as much as it marks Japan's wish to distance itself from China. This is the *kanji* (Chinese character) officially adapted for the written words *Kigen setsu*.

[36] The year 1909.

18
A Good Bargain

"**O**ver there, you know, chestnuts are plentiful. As for the price, well, let's say it must be about a yen for four *shō*,[37] more or less. Once it has arrived there—just imagine!—a *shō* is worth one yen fifty sen! Well, while I was there, along came an order for one thousand, eight hundred bags. If everything goes well, the price of a *shō* may rise to two yen and over, so I hastened to get in on the deal.

Once the one thousand and eight hundred bags were ready, I followed the order myself as far as Yokohama. The purchasers, I should say, were Chinese, and the whole lot was to be sent to their country. At this juncture, a Chinese arrived and stated that everything was in order. I was surprised that the formalities took up so little time, but now they were bringing up an enormous barrel about two meters in height and placing it in front of the depot, after which they filled it with water. 'Why?' you will ask. I myself did not understand their purpose in doing so. At all events, in view of its tremendous size, filling it was no simple task, believe me! Now I remember, yes, it took at least half a day!

I wondered what would happen next. Well, just think, they opened the bags and tipped all the chestnuts into the barrel. I was stupefied. No, really, these Chinese were up to all sorts of tricks! Because afterwards I realized what was going on. You see, when you put chestnuts in water, the good ones sink to the bottom while the damaged ones remain on the

---

[37] Equivalent to approximately 7.2 liters.

surface. Those crafty Chinese put them in bamboo panniers and rapidly deducted their weight from that shown on the labels! They got through the lot as quickly as possible. I saw it all myself, and was in a cold sweat! Consider that about one-seventh of the chestnuts were ruined! I was in a mess! The trans-action left me with a serious loss. What about the wormy ones, you ask? Being in a rage, I sold those, too; yes, I flogged off the lot. As they were Chinese, they acted as if nothing had happened. They tied up the straw sacks with cord and—I suppose—dispatched most of them to China.

"And then again, I once had occasion to purchase sweet potatoes at four yen a sackful—a contract for two thousand sacks. But the order arrived in the middle of the month, on the 14th, and delivery was to be made on the 25th, and even if I had worked myself into the ground it would have been absolutely impos-sible to supply two thousand sacks by that date. To be frank, however, I was really very sorry to have to let this order go. But then the senior member of the firm's staff told me, 'You know, it is true the contract says the 25th, but the date is not something to which one must adhere too rigorously.' He sounded con-vincing, and in the end I let myself be persuaded. No, no, the sweet potatoes were not intended for China. They were to go to America. You see, there are people who like sweet potatoes in America, too! It's certainly a funny world! In short, I decided to purchase what was needed. The sweet potatoes came from Saitama—yes, from Kawagoe. Only you see, although two thousand sacks do not in them-selves seem an enormous quantity, once one has definitely purchased them it makes quite a lot! Finally, after the 28th I had succeeded in making up the quantity stipulated in the contract, I presented myself and—I am not just saying it—some people really are crafty! One of the clauses in the contract provided for a penalty of eight thousand yen in damages and interest if the period was exceeded to any appreciable extent. And there was my customer claiming that he was bringing this clause into operation and—on top of that—failing to pay me! I admit I had been paid four thousand yen on account. During all this palaver, the sweet potatoes had already been loaded on to the boat, and there was nothing more to be done. Well, you can believe me or not, as you wish, I was so frustrated that I paid a surety of a thousand yen and carried out the formalities required to recover the goods. I thought I had won.

"But one always comes up against some superior obstacle! The other party deposited eight thousand yen by way of surety and then let the boat depart without any guarantee of the rest! In the end, it went to court, but I was powerless, as the clause duly appeared in the contract. So I dissolved into tears before the judge, pointing out that I was not only being deprived of my sweet potatoes but on top of that I had lost the case. How could I accept such an absurdity. Just put yourself in my place—do take account of the circumstances! Yes, that's what I said to him. I could see perfectly well that in his heart of hearts the judge was on my side, but the law came out on top and I finally lost."

19
The Procession

I looked up from my work somewhat mechanically and glanced towards the door. It had swung half open without my noticing, so that I could now see part of the long corridor, about sixty centimeters. It ended in a Chinese-style guardrail, followed by a door, the upper half of which was glass. Down from the sky came dense sunlight, and in the diagonal of the canopies, after passing over the tiles, it added patches of light to the front of the veranda, its warm rays then extending to the floor under my desk. I spent a few moments contemplating the sunrays, and like the light mist spreading before my eyes, the feeling that spring was here increased in intensity.

Then, within these few dozen centimeters, something of about the same height as the guardrail came into sight. A braided ribbon ornamented with arabesques, white on a red background, fitted lightly round the forehead as far as the roots of the hair, and all around was stitching depicting tiny eglantines with their little green leaves. The little button-shaped flowers stood out clearly against the black hair, like large drops from a delicate rose. Done up as far as the chin, which was almost hidden by the collar, a violet kimono swept airily along the corridor. The sleeves, hands and feet remained invisible. The silhouette furtively crossed the patch of sunlight as if escaping from it. Behind....

This time it was not so high. The head and shoulders were covered with a thick scarlet fabric and the larger back had a diagonal series of bamboo leaf motifs. In the middle of the chest, one single green leaf stood out against the charcoal-colored background. This shows the size of the bamboo leaf, larger than the feet treading the floorboards of the corridor. These little feet in their red shoes hardly touched the floor. After two or three steps, the short silhouette had silently traversed the space in front of my desk.

The third hood was of fabric with white and blue squares. The face under the flap was well rounded with full cheeks. It was dark red, like a very ripe apple. The arch of the eye, of which only the end could be made out, took a sharp downward turn, and a little nose, standing out slightly from the rounded cheek, was thrust forward. Everything except the face was enveloped in fabric with yellow stripes. The long sleeves trailed over the veranda and measured about three inches. This time the ground was being tapped with a bamboo cane taller than the person. After the cane I noticed the feather on the hair shining in the sunlight. No sooner had the lining of the yellow-striped garment sweeping along the veranda given off a silvery reflection than it disappeared.

Immediately behind this, a completely white face came into view. The whiteness began on the forehead, covered the flat cheeks and rose from the chin to the earlobe, the whole being as motionless as a wall. Only the pupils moved. Several layers of rouge on the lips produced a bluish play of light on the mouth. The color of the front of the garment was that of pigeon plumage. Looking at the bottom hem, I noticed a little violin and a large bow solemnly carried on its owner's shoulder. At the moment when two feet passed in front of my door, a square of black satin, placed on the back, with central embroidery of gold thread, stood out in the sunlight.

The final apparition was tiny. The little body looked as if it were about to fall under the sloping part. On the other hand, the face was broad. The largest part of all was the skull. A multi-colored crown had been placed on it. The diadem looked very tall. The body was enveloped in a short-sleeved garment with patterns of interesting lines, while grayish-mauve velvet fringes covered the shoulders and extended down to the small of the back, forming a triangle. The feet were encased in red *tabi*.[38] The Korean fan held in the hand was almost half the size of the body. It had a reflecting surface, lacquered in red, blue and yellow.

The procession had passed noiselessly in front of me. At the moment when I was feeling depressed, in the fading light of the sun entering my study through the partly open door and covering over a meter of the veranda, the sound of a violin came from the opposite side. It was accompanied by bursts of children's laughter.

My children amuse themselves day after day with these monkey tricks, playing havoc with their mother's *haori* and other pieces of material.

---

[38] A sort of sock, attached by hooks at the side and keeping the big toe separate from the other toes.

20
In Bygone Days

In the Valley of Pitlochry,[39] it was mid-autumn. October brought its warm hues to the fields and woods that caught the eye. In this light, life was present. The sun, halfway across the sky, embraced the calm air of the valley but its rays did not shine directly on to the ground. And neither did it neglect the other side of the mountains. It remained motionless, without the slightest movement, above the village in which there was not the slightest breath of wind. In the interval, the color of the fields and woods underwent a gradual change. Like the fruit that had been green the day before and was now as sweet as honey, the entire valley was in the process of ripening.

The Valley of Pitlochry belongs to the days of a hundred or two hundred years ago and settles down without resistance under a patina of dullness. The faces bronzed by autumn turn towards the sky and contemplate the clouds passing above the mountains. These clouds are at once white, then gray. Through their transparent background one can frequently see the hillsides, no matter at what moment one looks at them. These clouds seem as if they have always been there.

The house that welcomed me was at the top of a hill and provided a good viewing point for the clouds and the valley. It faced south and the sun bathed every part of its walls. At the western end, where

---

[39] In October 1902, towards the end of his educational stay in England, Sōseki toured Scotland.

everything was dried up and gray, one solitary rose tree, between the cold wall and the soft sun, bore a few roses. The enormous upside-down corolla undulated like a golden yellow wave, and in certain places the petals closed up as if to hide themselves. Their perfume, sucked up by the pale rays of the sun, was soon absorbed into the atmosphere. Standing in this space of three or four meters, I looked up. The roses had climbed to a fair height. The gray wall extended further than the stems of the rose tree could reach. Where it touched the roof there was a turret. The sun directed its rays from behind the thick fog above it.

At my feet, the slope descended towards the Valley of Pitlochry, and a good way down I could see a plain with vivid colors on the other side of the hill, stretching towards the mountains. The golden leaves of the birch trees combined to form a harmony of colors, infinitely enriched with the most pleasing shades. A black diagonal extended waves across the light, rust-colored hue reflected on the whole valley. The water of the valley, containing peat, was of an antique color, as if it had been used to dilute dyeing powder. It was the first time since I had arrived in this remote spot in the mountains that I had seen a stream of this color.

Behind me, the bailiff had just arrived on the scene. His beard, with the October light playing on it, seemed three-quarters white. His clothing was also somewhat unusual. He wore a kilt. The fabric was patterned with wide intersecting stripes, like the rug one puts over one's knees for a journey in a carriage. The folds went straight down as far as the knees, like a wide pair of trousers without a crotch, and his ankles were hidden in thick woolen socks. The folds of the kilt shook at each step and the flesh between the knee and thigh could be seen. It was a *hakama* of the old-world type, not ashamed of exposing the flesh.

My host carried hooked to his belt a little bag made of fur, of the same size as the gong struck by the bonzes during their prayers. When evening came, he pulled his chair up to the fireplace and, gazing at the crackling red embers, took a pipe and tobacco out of this little bag, and puffed away till very late. The bag is called a sporran.

We went down the ravine together and stepped on to a somber road. The evergreen leaves of the tree known as the Scotch fir seemed to be covered with tiny flakes. A squirrel had run up the tree trunk, waving his broad, bushy tail. A moment later, another squirrel had climbed on to the old thick moss, in a hurry to escape our gaze. The thick moss had not moved. The squirrel's tail disappeared into the darkness like a flywhisk, sliding over the blackish trunk.

The bailiff turned towards me and pointed towards the Valley of Pitlochry, clothed in light. Just as before, the dark river ran through the middle. He explained that if one went back up towards the north about one and a half leagues, one would come upon the Killiecrankie Gorges.

At the Battle of Killiecrankie, fought between the Highlanders and Lowlanders in the Valley of Killiecrankie, corpses piled up among the rocks held back the water flowing through the valley. Laden with the blood of the combatants, the red water of the river drained into the Valley of Pitlochry for three whole months.

I decided to leave early the next morning to visit the old Killiecrankie battlefield. When we left the ravine, a few rose petals lay scattered on the ground.

21
The Voice

It is now three days since Toyosaburo arrived at this boarding house. On the first day, as the sun was going down, he was fully occupied in arranging his belongings and sorting out his books. He then went to the public baths of the district, and fell asleep immediately after returning to his room. On the following day, on returning from the university, he sat down at this table and started to glance through a book, but, perhaps because of the sudden change of venue, he was unable to concentrate. The unceasing sound of a saw could be heard through the window.

Without changing his position, Toyosaburo stretched out his arm and opened a *shoji*. Right in front of him a gardener was industriously pruning the branches of a paulownia. As he cut off the overgrown branches, they fell undamaged to the ground. The numerous white places left by the saw stood out in stark contrast. At the same time, a greater stretch of the bare sky was visible as if it had come from afar in order to concentrate on the window. Supporting his cheek on one arm, Toyosaburo continued, without really knowing why, to contemplate the beautiful autumn sky far above the crown of the tree.

When Toyosaburo's gaze moved from the tree to the sky, his native country came to mind as clearly as a black point, and calm returned to him little by little. The image was remote, but he saw it as distinctly as if it were on his table.

At the foot of the mountain could be seen a large thatched roof, and it was before the gate of this house that the road ended after it had risen about four hundred meters from the village. It was high enough for a horse to pass underneath it. By the side of the *kura*[40] was a clump of chrysanthemums. The horse, its little bell tinkling, had disappeared behind the white wall. The roof tiles gleamed in the sun, which was high in the sky. The glistening trunks of the pines hid the whole of the mountain beyond from view. It was the season for gathering bamboo shoots. Toyosaburo had savored the scent of the freshly gathered shoots on the table and had heard his mother's voice, "Toyo! Toyo!" This voice came from far away and yet he heard it as clearly as if it were close by. His mother had died five years ago.

Toyosaburo, as if suddenly awakened, rubbed his eyes. The crown of the paulownia which he had been contemplating earlier was now once again reflected in his pupils. As the growing branches were always sawn off in the same place, their roots had disappeared under the knots and had acquired ugly shapes because of the force applied to them. Once again, Toyosaburo felt that he was being pushed towards his desk. On the other side of the paulownia, looking down towards the hedges, one noticed three or four shabby-looking *nagaya*. Someone had taken advantage of the autumn sunshine to put out a sofa, its stuffing falling out. Standing to one side, a woman of about fifty was looking up at the crown of the paulownia.

The stripes of her kimono were beginning to fade here and there. Her thin hair was held in place by a comb. She continued to stand there, a vague expression in her eyes, looking at the top of the tree

[40] A fireproof structure in which precious paintings, manuscripts and other important documents are kept.

with its sparse branches. Toyosaburo looked at her.

The old woman's face was pale and puffy. Her small, narrow eyes were shielded by heavy lids. She raised her head and directed a strange glance at Toyosaburo. He immediately turned his head away and fixed his eyes on his table.

On the third day, Toyosaburo went to the florist's and brought back some chrysanthemums. He would have preferred to have had some like those that flowered in the garden of the house where he was born, but he could not find any and so had to be satisfied with what the florist could offer. He bought three, simply tying them together with a straw and placing them in a vase shaped like a saké bottle. From the bottom of his wickerwork case he took out a little roll of silk, hand-painted by Hoashi Banri,[41] and hung it on the wall. He had expressly brought it from his home as an ornament for his room, after his trip to his native province the year before. He then sat down on a cushion and spent a few moments looking at the picture and the flowers. Then, from the direction of the *nagaya*, under the window, he heard a voice calling "Toyo! Toyo!" It was unmistakably the same voice and tone, and as full of tenderness as his mother's in his native land. Toyosaburo brusquely pushed aside the *shōji*. It was the woman he had seen the day before, with her pale, puffy face, in the already fading autumn sunlight, making a sign with her hand to an urchin of some twelve years of age. As the dry click of the *shōji* was heard, the woman turned her head and raised her heavy eyelids, looking in Toyosaburo's direction.

---

[41] Hoashi Banri (1778–1852), a scientist and Confucianist writer.

22
Money

After I had read five or six novels which were like a jumble of sensational news items, I felt totally sickened. At mealtimes, life's difficulties seemed to rest with all their weight on the lining of my stomach, along with the food. With the stomach full and heavy, the suffering is intolerable. I took my hat and went to call on the venerable Kūkoku.[42] He is a curious character, with something of the philosopher and something of the seer in him, and he is exactly the kind of man one wants to consult at such moments. "In the Universe, planets larger than Earth are exploding practically everywhere, and we need at least a hundred years to attain a knowledge of these celestial furnaces, so ..." he likes to tell us. He is among those who made light of the fire that broke out in Kanda. The fact is that Kūkoku's house was not destroyed.

Leaning against a little rectangular brazier, he was engaged in tracing something out in the ashes with a little brass stick.

"Well, still meditating, I see!" I called out.

"The fact is," he replied wearily, "I was having a little think about this thing called money."

"Fancy having come all this way just to hear someone talk about money!" I thought. I made no reply. Then, giving the impression of somebody who has just had a revelation, Kūkoku uttered the words "money is diabolical!"

Finding this observation far too trite I was content to reply "That's true!" without going further into it.

[42] A fictitious character.

Kūkoku traced a big circle in the middle of the ashes and stoked them, saying, "Listen to me. Let us imagine this is money. It can take on any number of possible shapes. If it is transformed into clothing, it can equally well take the form of food. It can equally well be converted into a train or into an inn."

"Nonsense! Doesn't everybody know that?"

"No—that's just it. Nobody truly realizes it. This circle"—and once again he drew a large one in the ashes—"can just as easily take the form of honesty or of its opposite. It can lead to Paradise and can just as easily lead to Hell. It is far too flexible, and civilization is not yet sufficiently advanced which is a great pity. Well then—when Humanity has made a little more progress, I am sure they'll reduce the amount in circulation."

"How will they do that?"

"It does not much matter how! For example, money will be divided into a number of colors. Yes, why not have red money, blue money, white money!"

"And then?"

"Then? Well, the red money must only be allowed to circulate inside the red sphere. The white money will only be used in the white zone. Limits will be assigned in such a way that outside its proper sphere, money will be no more use than broken tiles!"

If this had been our first meeting, and if Kūkoku had immediately made it his business to tell me this sort of story, I might have doubted his soundness of mind. But he is a man capable of seeing, in spirit, conflagrations of celestial bodies larger than Earth, and I therefore felt confident in asking him for his reasons. This was his reply.

"Considered from a certain angle, money is the symbol of work, is it not? But as work is in no case of the same nature as money, it is a major mistake to attempt to exchange it for the money which is assumed to represent it. For example, let us assume that I have mined ten thousand tons of coal. This is manual labor, and if I exchange it for money the only possible function of this money is to be exchanged for work of the same nature. However, once this work, which requires no reflection, has been converted into money, this conversion has hardly taken place before the money is suddenly endowed with the supernatural power of omnipotence and bartered without reduction for an activity based on mental intelligence. Finally, the spiritual world is thrown into confusion. Is it not therefore the most harmful kind of diabolical power? That is why a classification must be devised to enlighten mankind on this evil spell, no matter to how small an extent."

I signified my agreement with the principle of redistribution. Then, after a moment, I asked Kūkoku, "It is certainly dishonest to purchase mental labor by means of manual labor, but is not a person who allows himself to be bought likewise dishonest?"

"Yes, certainly! When I see how omniscient and omnipresent money has become, I feel there is nothing to be done, since God too has capitulated before man! Yes, truly, the God of modern times is nothing short of barbarous!"

After this spontaneous exchange of views with Kūkoku, I went home.

23
The Heart

I hung out the little wet bath towel on the first floor windowsill and looked down on the street bathed in the rays of the spring sun. A clog mender with a sparse white beard, his head covered in a hood, was just passing the hedge. He had attached an old tambourine to a yoke and was striking it with a bamboo stick, but the noise, though sonorous, lacked strength, like a memory gently passing through the mind.

On reaching the gate of the doctor's house on the opposite side of the street, the old man struck his little drum, which gave out a dull sound in the spring air. A bird flew out of the foliage of a pale plum tree, the blossom-colored branches of which stretched out above his head. The clog mender did not notice it. Proceeding along the green bamboo hedge, he returned towards the opposite side and disappeared. With one single beat of its wings, the bird flew to a spot just below the windowsill. It remained for a moment on the thin branch of a pomegranate tree, but it was visibly frightened. Then it changed its position three times. While doing so, it saw me resting against the railing and suddenly flew off. I hardly had time to notice that the top of the branch had performed a very slight movement when the bird landed with its delicate feet on one of the bars of the railing.

This was the first time I had seen this bird, and I was naturally unable to put a name to it, but I was strangely moved by the color of its plumage. Like the nightingale, it had wings of sober elegance and a dark red throat the color of brick. It was so delicate that at the slightest puff of air it would fly away. Thinking that it would be a crime to frighten it, I stayed there for some time, leaning against the windowsill, not even daring to move my little finger, and waited patiently. Contrary to my expectations, however, the bird did not appear to be in the least bit disturbed, and in the end I softly retreated backwards. At the same time, the bird jumped back on to the windowsill, right in front of my eyes. There was a distance of scarcely thirty centimeters between us. Almost reluctantly, I stretched out my hand towards that beautiful bird. As if placing its fate in my care, it accepted the proffered hand, placing in its hollow its tender wings, its delicate feet and its quivering throat. I looked at its little round head and thought, "This bird …" but did not succeed in finishing. The rest remained buried deep in my heart as if it were all slightly confused. If it were possible, by some mysterious power, to concentrate in one place everything at the bottom of one's heart and to distinguish the contours clearly … well, I felt it would be something of the same color as the bird I now held in the hollow of my hand. Yes, it would be the same. I immediately put the bird in a cage and became lost in contemplation until the shadow of the spring sun had lengthened. I wondered what the bird was feeling as it eyed me.

Very soon afterwards, I went for a walk. With a light heart, I wandered from street to street, further and further without any particular purpose, and reached the end of the populated thoroughfares, walking first towards the left, then towards the right, passing strangers, or passed by them, in an endless flow. It was in vain that I wandered so far, as the street was full of life, joyous and carefree, so that it did not even occur to me that the moment would come when I would sense a kind of repression in this contact with the outside world. I was happy to see thousands of people, but merely happy, and none of the physiognomies I saw impressed themselves, by their glances or by the shape of their noses, on my mind. Then, from somewhere or other came a noise like a bell suspended from the entrance to a temple knocking against the tiles of the porch roof. With a shout of surprise, I saw a woman standing at the entrance to a narrow little side street, about ten meters further on. I could hardly make out her clothing and her hairstyle. I could see only her face. That face, of which it was impossible to distinguish the various features separately—those eyes, that nose, those eyebrows, that forehead—had combined and shaped into a unique face for me alone. For a whole century—from time immemorial—the face had been waiting for me in that place, immutable: that nose, those eyes, those lips had waited for me. A hundred years later, that face would still draw me, further and further, docile and in thrall. In silence, the face controlled me. The woman turned round in silence. I joined her and found what I had taken for a narrow little side street was an alleyway so narrow and gloomy that normally I should have hesitated to enter it. But the woman did so unhesitatingly. She did not speak. However, she signaled to me to follow her. I made myself as small as I could and followed her into the alleyway.

A black *noren*[43] was gently fluttering in the breeze.

---

[43] A piece of fabric hung across the entrance to a shop or restaurant, serving as the sign to the establishment.

It bore a sign in white. My head brushed against the lamp fixed to the porch roof. In the middle was an emblem consisting of three superimposed pines with the character *moto*[44] underneath. I looked towards a glass jar full of little round tinkling bells. Then under the porch roof, I saw five or six prints in rectangular frames. Finally, a bottle of scent and the narrow passage led to the ink black walls of a *dozo*.[45] The woman stood less than a meter away from me. She turned to face me in one single movement. Then she suddenly turned to the right, and at this moment my mind underwent a sudden change and I identified myself with the bird I had encountered shortly before. I immediately followed the woman, then turned, as she herself did, to the right. Once I had turned, I found myself in a long alleyway, narrower and darker than the one before and stretching ahead as far as the eye could see. In accordance with the mute instructions given to me by the woman, I too entered the dark narrow passage to which there seemed no end. In turn, I disappeared.

[44] A Chinese character pronounced as *moto* or *hon,* but which is difficult to define.
[45] A godown with plastered walls.

24
Changes

Our tables were side by side in a cramped room on the first floor. The shiny appearance of the brownish *tatami* is still present in my memory after more than twenty-five years. The room faced north, and in front of the little window, which measured less than sixty centimeters, we studied in cramped conditions in an uncomfortable position, with our shoulders practically touching. When darkness fell, we braved the cold that invaded the room and drew back the *shōji* of the window. At such moments it would happen that in the house just below our window a young girl with a dreamy look would be standing behind the bamboo canes which protected her window. At the quiet hour when evening was coming on, her face and silhouette seemed to us to embody a particular beauty. I would often spend a minute or two in contemplation and murmur to myself, "Oh, how beautiful she is!" But I said nothing of this to Nakamura.[46] He, too, made no mention of it.

I have now completely forgotten the woman's face. I only have a vague feeling that she must have been the daughter of a carpenter or somebody similar. At all events, she was from a poor family and lived in a *nagaya*. As for us, our quarters were part of a *nagaya* and it would have been in vain to search for a single tile on the roof. About ten poor students like me were lodged on the ground floor, together with the manager. In the drafty hall we ate our meals with-

---

[46] Nakamura Yoshikoto, better known as Nakamura Zekō, Chairman of the Southern Manchurian Railway Company.

out removing our clogs. Our food cost only two yen a month, and it was very poor. On alternate days, however, we were served a meat soup. Of course, there was only a little piece of fat floating vaguely on the surface, and our only smell of meat was that left on our chopsticks. The boarders complained throughout the year of the manager's stinginess, saying that he should be ashamed of feeding us so badly.

Nakamura and I were coaches at this private college. We were paid a salary of five yen a month and had to teach for about two hours a day. For my part, I taught geography, with the help of manuals published in English, and geometry. In the geometry lessons, I was sometimes embarrassed at my lack of success in connecting up lines which were considered to be connected. But when I drew a complex figure in big strokes, the two lines in the end made one single line when superimposed on the blackboard, and this gave me a great deal of pleasure.

When we got up in the morning, we crossed the Ryogoku Bridge to attend the Hitotsubashi preparatory school. At that time, the fees were twenty-five sen a month. We both laid out our salary on the table any old how, twenty-five sen for our studies, two yen for our board, not forgetting a certain sum for the public baths, and then pocketed the remainder and went out to have a meal of noodles, *shiruko*[47] and *sushi*.[48] When our joint funds were exhausted, we remained confined to the house. One day, on our way to the preparatory school, while we were crossing the Ryogoku bridge, Nakamura asked me, "In the Western novel you are reading at present, are there any beautiful women?"

[47] Rice seasoned with sweetened vinegar, often with raw fish.
[48] A kind of thick soup with a base of sweetened red beans.

"Yes, beautiful women come into it," I replied. But I no longer remember what novel it was—or what type of beauty. Nakamura had at that time already become a man who did not read novels.

When Nakamura became champion of a boat race in which the school was victorious, the establishment rewarded us with a sum of money, which enabled me to buy books. One of these, I remember, bore the following inscription at the top, "This book has been presented in memory of ...". Nakamura had then said, "I do not need any books myself, but I will buy you what you want." And he made me a present of a treatise by Arnold[49] as well as Shakespeare's *Hamlet*. They are still in my possession. That was when I read *Hamlet* for the first time. I did not understand a word of it.

As soon as he left school, Nakamura embarked for Formosa, and we lost touch with each other for many long years before meeting again by chance in the very center of London. This was about seven years ago.[50] Nakamura had not changed at all, and he was very well off. Together we enjoyed all the distractions London had to offer. This time Nakamura did not ask me, as he had done formerly, whether beautiful women appeared in the Western novels I was reading. It was now he who waxed lyrical on the beautiful women of the West.

After returning to Japan, we once again lost touch, but this year, at the end of January, he sent some-

[49] Matthew Arnold (1822–1888), English poet and critic, a copy of whose work *Literature and Dogma* is to be found in Sōseki's library, conserved at Tokyo University.
[50] This was Sōseki's educational tour of England. He arrived in London on October 28th 1900 and returned to Tokyo on January 24th 1903.

body to ask me to meet him in Tsukiji, at the Shinkiraku[51] restaurant. He said he wanted to talk to me. He said "at midday", but by my watch it was already past eleven—and that very day there was a particularly fierce north wind. In the street the violence of the gusts was such that carriages seemed to be on the point of being lifted off the ground. I had to see to something which I wanted to get settled that same afternoon without fail. I asked my wife to telephone Nakamura and ask whether our meeting could not be postponed until the following day, but Nakamura also had certain things to see to, in addition to the still uncompleted preparations for his departure, so he too had no time. At this point, the telephone conversation was cut off. However hard I tried, it proved impossible to restore communication. "It's sure to be because of the wind!" said my wife, coming back into the room, looking perished with the cold, and our meeting never materialized.

The Nakamura of those days has since become Chairman of Mantetsu.[52] As for me, I became a writer. I have absolutely no idea of the activities of the Chairman of Mantetsu. As for Nakamura, he has probably not read a single page of any of my novels.

[51] A famous restaurant in Tokyo specializing in Japanese cuisine.
[52] Abbreviation of *Nan Manshu Tetsudo Kabushiki Gaisha*
(Southern Manchurian Railway Company.)

25
Craig[53] Sensei (Meiji 42)

Like a swallow, my teacher Mr Craig has his nest on the fourth floor. If one looks up from the street, it is impossible to see his window. After walking up the stairs with a slight pain in the thigh, one finally stands before his front door. This is not really a correct description, because it is simply a panel hardly three feet wide, painted in black, with a brass knocker. After standing still for a few moments, I give one rap at the door with the end of the knocker, "boom", then it is opened from the inside.

It is always the same woman who opens the door. She is shortsighted and wears glasses. She always looks frightened. She is about fifty years old, time enough to know the world, yet she always seems to be frightened. She looks surprised, but asks me to come in, so I am almost sorry to have disturbed her. She disappears as soon as I enter. The guest room of my teacher—for a long time I did not realize it was a guest room—is not really furnished. One sees only two windows and lots of books, nothing else. Here Mr Craig usually camps.

On seeing me, he calls out, "Well now!" extending his hand, a sign that I should take hold of it. I

---

[53] William James Craig (1843–1906), an authority on Shakespeare. At the end of 1879, he resigned his chair at the University of Aberystwyth, Wales, where his passion for literature had a profound influence on his students. Up until his death in London, he continued his research on Shakespeare. The volume devoted to *King Lear* in the forty-volume edition known as the *Arden Shakespeare,* and edited by Craig, is considered a *chef d'oeuvre.* Shortly before he died, he was working on a volume devoted to *Coriolanus*. He is buried at Reigate cemetery.

therefore clasp his hand, but he does not reciprocate. I cannot really say that this is conducive to a feeling of wellbeing in me. I would be glad if this formality would cease altogether. But conscientious as always when he sees me, he exclaims, "There!" Always this hairy hand, this passive hand, is extended towards me. How strange habits are!

This hand belongs to my teacher who answers so many questions. During our first meeting, I asked him what his fee was. Then he replied, looking quickly out of the window, "What do you think of seven shillings for one lesson? If it is too much, I would be willing to meet you." We agreed on seven shillings for one lesson, with payment at the end of each month. Sometimes it happens that my teacher suddenly asks me for money. "Sir, I need some money, could you pay me in advance?" I take some gold coins from my trouser pocket and hand them to him. "There, Sir." "I am sorry," he says, taking the money. He examines it for a moment, weighs it in the palm of his hand—that passive hand—and lets it disappear into his trouser pocket. He never thinks of returning the balance of my money, which often causes me embarrassment. If I try to deduct what I have overpaid from the next month's fee, I do not succeed, because in the same week he makes a new request, "I would like to buy some books."

As my teacher is an Irishman, his accent is difficult to understand. When he becomes excited, it sounds as if two people from Tokyo and Satsuma[54] are quarreling. Added to this, he is an extraordinarily inconsiderate, hasty and confused person. During a

[54] The western part of Japan, the present Kagoshima prefecture in Kyūshū Island.

discussion about a complicated subject, his words become so involved that I stop, stare at him and leave myself to my fate.

His face is extremely original. As a European, he has a high nose with a pronounced bridge which, because of its thickness, looks like mine, a nose which does not evoke a pleasant, cheerful impression. This is compensated for by the original impression which the uneven pell-mell of his features awakens. In particular, his beard, wild and neglected, almost provokes a feeling of regret in me. Yes, when I met him on Baker Street, he looked to me like a cab driver who had forgotten his whip.

He never wears a white shirt but year in and year out a check flannel shirt and felt slippers. He constantly stretches his slippered feet in front of the chimney fire, so close that it appears as if his feet touch the fire. At the same time, his hand slaps his knee. Suddenly, for the first time a gold ring on his massive hand flashes towards me. Now and again he strokes his hand, and in this way he gives the lesson. About what? That is difficult to say. If I listen to him silently, his flight of thought takes me wherever he likes without returning to the starting point. Also this flight relates to the time of the year and the weather. Very often I land with him on the North Pole, only suddenly to be put down on the South Pole. Today it is this, tomorrow something else. Without approaching his subject too closely, he chatters, but in order to save his honor he indulges in literary small talk. Of course he is right, because, if I think back, it seems to me impossible to give a polished systematic lecture for seven shillings. It was silly of me to make such a request. By the way, complete confusion reigns in my teacher's head, symbolically indicated by his beard.

It is perhaps just as well that I have not paid a higher fee in order to get an excellent lecture.

His strength is poetry. His face trembles, the upper part of his body shakes when he reads poems. Yes, truly. He doesn't think of reading something out loud for me, but he enjoys it for himself. In the end I am always the one who loses out. I once happened to have a book on Swinburne's[55] *Rosamund*. "Show it to me," he said. He read out some lines, let the book fall on his lap, put on his spectacles and complained, "Oh! Dear God, how sorry I am for Swinburne, he is no longer at his best writing such nonsense." At that time, I wanted to read his masterpiece, *Atalanta in Calydon*.

Altogether, this Mr Craig treats me like child. "Do you know this?" or "Do you understand this?", he asks. He asks me quite simple, stupid questions. On the other hand, he suddenly considers me as his colleague, asking me a very difficult question. Thus once he read Watson's[56] poem to me and asked, "There are two opinions about this poem, one says that it comes very close to Shelley, whereas the other definitely disputes this. Who do you think is right?" How can I solve this question? I can only read European poems with my eyes and repeat them aloud and in this way allow their sound to affect my ear. Only then do I arrive at the right understanding. I therefore answer haphazardly. I cannot remember whose view I represented. But what affected me embarrassingly, comically, was that Mr Craig as usual slapped his knee with the hand and said, "Look, I am

---

[55] Algernon Charles Swinburne (1837–1909), English lyric poet and critic. His *Essays and Studies* (1875) and *Studies in Prose and Poetry* (1894) are among his chief critical works.
[56] William Watson (1858–1935), English poet.

also of your opinion."

One day he looked out of the window on to the street and remarked, "Look how many people wander about and how few of them have the capacity to enjoy the beauty of poetry. Probably hardly one out of a hundred. Poor people! On the whole, English people are insensitive to poetry. Irish people are nobler—yes, more refined. We both must be considered lucky, because we understand poetry."

I should have really thanked Mr Craig for his compliment because he counted me among those who understood poetry, but the way he treated me remained very condescending. I was never able to discover any warmth of feeling; for me he remained a person prattling on mechanically.

But one thing I must not leave unsaid. I did not feel happy in my boarding house and therefore was considering whether to ask Mr Craig if I could come and stay with him.[57] One day, after the lecture was finished, I asked him. He unintentionally slapped his knee with the hand and exclaimed, "Splendid, come with me. I will show you around." He took me quickly through the dining room, the maid's room, the kitchen, etc. Mr Craig's flat is just a corner of the fourth floor and of course not roomy. After two to three minutes, we had inspected all the rooms. Mr Craig returned to the guest room and I was expecting a refusal, "Sir, the flat is too small. As you can see I have no room." Instead, he suddenly started to speak about Walt Whitman. "Whitman visited me a few years ago and stayed a while with me." I could not

---

[57] A system which was still very widespread in Japan at the time, whereby a student lodged with a family or with a professor, for example, performing certain tasks in return.

understand him properly because he was speaking so quickly, but he probably meant that Whitman visited him and not the other way around. "When I first read his poetry, it left no impression on me. However after reading it over and over again, I became more and more interested, and his poems became my favorites. Therefore...."

The idea of going to stay with him had evaporated. I simply let everything take its course, listened to him quietly, and said "yes" now and again. If I am not wrong, there was a question of a dispute between Shelley and some Mr X. "Here there must be no dispute. Both are equally close to me, and because I love them equally, they should get on together," he protested. He can protest as much as he likes, but it is purposeless to dwell on a dispute which broke out many years ago.

My teacher becomes very confused and easily forgets where he has put his books, etc. If he cannot find a book immediately, he becomes impetuous and screams frantically for the old woman in the kitchen as if the place is on fire. The old woman then storms into the guest room looking frantic.

"Oh, where did you put my Wordsworth?"

The big frightened eyes of the old woman move over the bookcase. Despite looking disturbed, she has great presence of mind, because she immediately discovers the "Wordsworth" and holds it under her master's nose saying, with a slight reproach, "Here, Sir." Mr Craig simply tears it out of her hand, with two fingers knocks on the dirty cover and starts, "Wordsworth...." Still looking frightened, the old woman disappears into the kitchen. For several minutes Mr Craig's fingers slap the cover without opening the book which was found with such difficulty.

Now and again, my teacher writes to me. His handwriting puzzles me. Although he writes only a few lines and I have time to decipher them, I am absolutely unable to do so. Anyhow, since in my experience, such a letter always announces the cancellation of a lesson, I decide, rightly, to save myself the effort of deciphering it. Although that old lady seldom writes on behalf of Mr Craig, when she does the writing is like copperplate. What an asset to her employer! Mr Craig complained to me that his writing was bad and added that mine was far better.

What terrible ink spots may occur if somebody with such handwriting writes a manuscript? I believe that Mr Craig is the editor of the *Arden Shakespeare*. I cannot believe that such handwriting can be converted into print. Nevertheless, he is quite indifferent. In addition, he suggested that I should read his introduction to *Hamlet*. During my next visit, I told him that it had interested me very much, whereupon he urged me to recommend the book when I returned to Japan. *Hamlet* in the *Arden Shakespeare* has been of inestimable help to me during my lectures at the Japanese University. There is probably no other book whose annotations reach such profundity and hit the mark, a fact of which I was not aware at the time. His knowledge of Shakespeare astounded me.

If one turns from the guest room at a right angle, one knocks against a study the size of six *tatami* mats. More accurately, his apartment forms a small corner of the fourth floor. Right at the end of this corner, an irreplaceable treasure is hidden. There lie many exercise books with blue covers, one and a half feet long, one foot wide. Untiringly, he transfers into them all his notes made on slips of paper. It is his life-long pleasure to see the space in his copybooks slowly but continuously filled—like a miser who saves small old coins. After a few visits to my teacher, I knew that these blue copybooks formed the manuscript of a Shakespeare dictionary. I heard that he had sacrificed his position as Professor of Literature at a certain university in Wales in order to finish this dictionary. It is therefore no wonder that a man who has given up a professorship considers his student, who pays him a fee of only seven shillings, of secondary importance. The Shakespeare dictionary is buried in his head and is foaming and fermenting there day and night.

I asked him once whether he shouldn't rest content with the Schmidt[58] dictionary instead of bestowing on the world his superfluous book. My teacher could hardly control his contempt. He brought the dictionary to me with the words, "Have a look at it." Then I saw that page after page of the much-praised two-volume dictionary was full of written corrections. "My God," I exclaimed, my bewildered eyes staring at the book. Mr Craig felt very uplifted. "Lord, if I could have wanted to write a book like this one, I could have saved myself the trouble." With both fingers he slapped violently on the paper showing black marks

"Since when have you been working on this?"

My teacher got up, went towards the bookcase opposite and tried to find something eagerly but unsuccessfully. Even before the old woman appeared, he asked excitedly as always, "Jane, where

[58] Alexander Schmidt (1816–1887), German linguist and author of a Shakespeare lexicon published in 1902.

did you put my Dowden?"[59] Frightened as usual, the old woman came in and with a reproachful "Here, Sir!" she disappeared. Without taking any notice of her, he opened the book eagerly; "Ah ha! Here it is. Dowden hasn't forgotten my name. 'Mr Craig, who exclusively devotes himself to the study of Shakespeare.' This book was published in 187... and my studies lie even further back...." The presence of my teacher gripped me. Once I asked him when it would be finished. "That only God knows. In any case, I will work on it as long as I breathe." Then he put the Dowden in its old place.

A short time after this, I stopped visiting him. One day before my last visit, he said to me, "Is there no place for a professor in Japan? If I were younger, I would like to go there." With this, his face became resigned as if the uncertainty of all earthly things deeply affected him. That was the only time that a trace of sentimentality flitted over his face. "You are still young," I said to him. "Oh no, who knows what the next moment will bring. I am already fifty-six years old." He remained introspective.

About two years after my return, a newly arrived journal for literature and art published the news of the death of Mr Craig, with a short remark that he had been a Shakespeare researcher. I put the journal to one side and thought that the dictionary had never been finished but remained only a fragment.

[59] Edward Dowden (1843–1913), professor of English literature and author of a study on Shakespeare published in 1825 which became a recognized work of reference.

26
The Carlyle[60] Museum
(Meiji 38)[61]

In a corner of the park,[62] a man is haranguing the passersby. At the other end, an elderly man with bent shoulders, clad in a coat that has seen better days and holding in his hand a hat the shape of a sugar loaf, has stopped in his tracks to take a look at the speaker. The latter suddenly pauses in his speech and walks quickly over to the man with the air of some village dignitary standing opposite him. The speaker asks him in hoarse tones and with a rustic accent, "You wouldn't be Carlyle, by any chance?"

"Indeed," the learned man replies, "I am."

The other continues, "Is it really you who are known as the Chelsea Sage?"[63]

"Yes, it would seem so."

"And yet that's the name of a bird! A human being called that is something very rare! I've never come across that before!" With these words, the speaker

---

[60] Thomas Carlyle (1795–1881), Scottish historian, critic and philosopher. Influenced by the German writers (Goethe, Schiller, Herder), he became famous with his *History of the French Revolution* (1837) and his work *On Heroes, Hero Worship and the Heroic in History* (1841). He contributed much to the development of the study of German thought in England.
[61] 1905.
[62] Hyde Park.
[63] Literally "wise" in the text transcribed into Japanese with the aid of two *kanji* (idiograms) meaning "philosopher" (*tetsujin*), to which Sōseki gives an approximate English pronunciation (seidz). This makes it possible to preserve the full sense of the play on words based on the homonymy of this term, often used ironically in English in the sense of "sage" (wise) and sage grouse, which is a Scottish red grouse (capercaillie, Scottish hazel grouse).

gives a great burst of laughter and the great man replies, "True enough. If everybody is just a human being like all the others, to saddle a man with the nickname 'Sage' is to call him a bird. All things considered, it is preferable to be regarded as a normal human being!" And he, in turn, bursts out laughing.

On each of my walks in the park before dinner, I sit down on a seat by the edge of the river and look towards the opposite bank. A fog of the kind that only belongs to London seems to delight in haunting the banks. I look straight in front of me, my chin resting on my cherry wood walking stick. The distant shadows shrouding the opposite bank become thicker and thicker, lengthening out and forming a border around the base of a four-storied house. In the end all that is left is an intangible speckled veil lingering in the sky, meeting the gaze like something that has arrived from a far-off world of the future. Then, from the depth of this turtledove grayness, glimmers appear one by one, like drops of water shining with a subdued gleam. On the second and third and then on the fourth floor of the dwelling, the lights come on. I then quietly make my way to my boarding house, tapping the pavement with my stick. Every day when twilight comes, the story of the speaker and Carlyle returns to my mind. For it is here, in this fog-bound spot with a few gleams of light passing through it, that the philosopher once lived. It is Chelsea.

Carlyle is no longer living. The speaker, too, is doubtless dead. But Chelsea exists as it did in the past. More than that, the house which he inhabited for many long years is still there, ceremoniously preserved. I do not know how many celebrities it welcomed within its walls, to how many it bid farewell after 1708, when Cheyne Row appeared. But no matter, it remains unchanged, as in its past. It was due to the initiative of a person of eminence that after Carlyle's demise the objects which he had used throughout his life were collected together, as well as his books and documents, and were distributed throughout the various rooms so that admirers or simply the curious would be able to visit this place at their leisure and as their fancy took them.

To mention but a few men of letters among the most famous associated with Chelsea, Thomas Moore is the first who springs to mind, followed more recently by Smollett[64] and—still closer to our times and a contemporary of Carlyle—by Leigh Hunt.[65] Hunt's house was in the immediate neighborhood of Carlyle. The latter, moreover, relates in his memoirs how Hunt paid him a visit on the very evening he moved in. It is also known that Hunt presented Carlyle's wife with a portrait of Shelley. In addition to the famous people already mentioned, the house inhabited by Eliot, and also the home of Rossetti, are near by, both of them on the walk that borders the river. But all these residences have changed hands. They are now inhabited and thus cannot be visited. It is only Carlyle's old hermitage that can be explored at will, for a charge of six pence, whoever the visitor and whatever the hour.

Cheyne Row is a lane forking out to the south of

[64] Tobias Smollett (1721–1771), Scottish novelist. His peregrinations in Jamaica formed the basis of his *Adventures of Roderick Random* (1748), followed by his *Adventures of Peregrine Pickle* (1751).

[65] James Henry Leigh Hunt (1784–1859), English journalist and poet. His poetry, owing to a certain liberty of vocabulary, was regarded as full of slang. See *Narrative Poems* (1832). In Italy, he founded the *Liberal* (1822–3) with Byron, whom he introduced to Shelley and Keats.

the thoroughfare that extends along the river bank, and Carlyle's house, No. 24, is on the right, towards the middle of the alley.

One morning, although I had up to then been content to look along the embankment at fog-bound Chelsea, I crossed the bridge and knocked at the door of this famous hermitage.

The word "hermitage" suggests an atmosphere pervaded by relics. At the very least, the picture evoked is inevitably associated with ideas of sober elegance or even refinement. But Carlyle's hermitage gives no impression of fragility or affectation. It is a square three-storied house built so close to the pavement that one only needs to stretch out one's arm to reach the door knocker.

It is absolutely straight, like the chimney of a large factory cut open at the base and then roofed, the windows having been added afterwards.

This, then, is the house that Carlyle finally discovered after a long and unsuccessful search when he found himself in London for the first time after leaving his countryside in the north. He searched in the south. He searched in the west and to the north of Hampstead, to no avail, before he finally found himself in Cheyne Row. He nevertheless lacked the determination to make a firm choice. He who mocked not only the forty million simpletons who inhabited England, but also the entire world, had to send a communication to ascertain the wishes of his wife, although she, too, was included among the nincompoops. Here is the reply that Carlyle's wife addressed to her husband: "As regards your entry into accommodation, if the houses which you have seen are both to your liking I would wish that you would reserve them until I shall be in London. Nonetheless, if this be found not to be possible, I shall in no way reproach you, and I ask you to choose one of them yourself, without waiting upon my arrival in London. Do as you judge best." Thus, Carlyle, who maintained that he had need of no one else when drafting and revising his writings, was conscious of the necessity of asking his wife's opinion before making a definite choice of residence. He thus awaited her arrival in the capital before coming to a decision. Mrs Carlyle arrived four days later. This time it was together that they explored the city in all directions, from north to south, from east to west, before concluding that it was Cheyne Row that suited them. They moved in on June 10th 1834, and we even know that they were accompanied by their servant bearing a cage containing canaries. Why had Mrs Carlyle's choice fallen on this house? Was it because it had specially taken her fancy? Was there no other that suited her? Be that as it may, it was this square house the shape of a chimney, with an annual rent of three hundred and fifty yen, that welcomed the new occupants within its walls. And it was here that Carlyle lived in austerity, like Cromwell, like the Emperor Frederick, in this house resembling a factory chimney, without even receiving the annual income offered him by Disraeli for the publication of his writings in which both Cromwell and the Emperor Frederick were celebrated.

And now here I am standing on the stone steps of this square edifice and lifting up the knocker in the image of an ogre. A few moments later, a corpulent woman of some fifty years of age makes her appearance and bids me enter. She seems to have immediately recognized me as a visitor. Very soon she produces something that looks like a register and asks me to enter my name. I recollect having paid four separate visits to this house during my stay in London and written my name in the book all four times. This was the first time. I wanted to sign my name as carefully as possible, but only succeeded in doing so in my customary poor writing. I looked quickly through the book and found that no Japanese name appeared. So I was the first Japanese to come here! This unimportant detail pleased me. The woman told me to follow her and gestured to me to open a door on the left, which gave access to a room looking on to the street. It appeared that in former times it had been a drawing room. It contained a variety of objects. Pictures and photographs hung on the walls, most of them portraits of the Carlyle couple. The next room contained a library which had been designed by Carlyle himself. It was filled with books, some weighty and others trivial. On some of them, time had left its patina, while there were others which for me were illegible. Likewise, on show were a medal of silver and another of copper which were struck on the occasion of Carlyle's eighteenth birthday. No gold medal seems to have been produced. To contemplate the time lag between the existence of these engraved medals, imperturbable in their useless durability, and the man to whom they were presented, whose life vanished as if in a puff of smoke, is to experience a feeling which, to say the least, is somewhat strange. I then went up to the first floor. Here again I found a large library with stacks of books. For me they were either illegible, unknown or useless. It appears that this room likewise once served as a drawing room. The exhibits included a letter written to Carlyle by Bismarck, together with a Prussian Cross, no doubt obtained through the favor

of the Emperor Frederick. Mrs Carlyle's bed stood in
this room. It was reduced to extreme simplicity and
was bare of any ornaments.

My guide resembled the guides of all countries.
For a little while now, she had been inundating me
with explanations concerning all the articles conserved in every room. This occupation had probably
not been her speciality for fifty years, but she
showed considerable competence. On such and such
a day of such a month in the year so and so, the
following happened.... The words tumbled out of her
mouth unceasingly. But that was not all. This elo-
quence showed variations, giving rise to a rhythm.
As the tones were pleasant, one had only to listen,
without any longer understanding what she said. At
the beginning, I did try to put questions to her, but in
the end I found this exhausting, and I adapted the
attitude of a person who looks at whatever he wants
to see, making it clear to her that she was at liberty
to deliver as many speeches as she wished but would
be powerless to impede my freedom. For her part,
the good woman patiently continued with her "such
and such a day of such and such a month" with an air
of "I give my explanations, whether people listen or
not...".

I put my head out of the window situated to the
east and looked at the surroundings. Beneath me was
a garden of about thirty square meters. Both to the
left and to the right, as well as in the front, the house
was surrounded by high stone walls which in their
turn formed another square. I found myself wondering whether the square was perhaps the indispensable element of this house. Yet, there was nothing
square about Carlyle's face. It was more reminiscent
of a steep cliff of which the central part had

collapsed and remained clinging to the grassy ground. His wife's face made one think of a good-quality shallot. As for my guide, her face was round and reddish like a flavored bread roll. While I was looking at her and thinking to myself that she certainly had a rotund countenance, she started off once more with "such and such a day of such and such a month". And I once again looked out of the window.

Carlyle wrote, "The view from the window at the back of the house is limited to the green abundance of the grass in the fields and to the steep red roof outlined between the leaves. In this season, when the wind blows from the west, the countryside gives an impression of gratefulness and good cheer and creates a feeling of well-being." As I, for my part, was keen to see the rich foliage and the green fields, I leaned out of the window in question. I repeated the attempt, but in vain. No wealth of leaves presented itself to my gaze. I just saw houses, nothing but houses on all sides, above which loomed, as if unwillingly, a sickly looking leaden sky. I drew back my head with some difficulty through the small gap left by the window. My guide's voice was still resounding with "such and such a day of such and such a month in the year so and so".

Carlyle also writes, "If one looks in the direction of London, one sees the top of the tower of Westminster Abbey and the dome of St Paul's Cathedral. Nothing more, unless it be the Palace, which appears and disappears as the soot-colored smoke allows, like a ghostly apparition."

The expression "in the direction of London" is by now obsolete. It is rather like saying, "Today I came to Chelsea and saw London," or "Sitting at home, I look towards the house." It is little different from the absurd reasoning of wanting to look in one's own direction with one's own eyes. But the fact is that Carlyle did not consider that he lived in London. His wish was to view the monuments of the center of the capital from his country retreat. For the third time, I looked out of the window and directed my gaze to what he meant by London. But I saw neither Westminster nor St Paul's. Thousands of houses seemed to jostle one another, hundreds of thousands of people wandered hither and thither, millions of noises assailed the air. The Chelsea of 1834 and that of today have nothing in common. I once again withdrew from the window. The good woman was behind me, standing still and waiting in silence.

We went up to the second floor. In a corner of the room, Carlyle's bed indifferently barred the way. Blue curtains hung tranquilly down from the canopy, and the interior, now without purpose, was soundless in the half light. I do not know what wood was used for the manufacture of this bed, but it was hard to discern any special feature in it. All one can say is that the work was sober, if not actually plain. It gave an idea of the circumstances of its one-time occupant. The basin in which he washed was placed beside it with the same respect that is accorded to the sacred treasures of the ancient court of China. Although the object was presumably intended for bathing, it was in fact nothing more than a large bucket. When one thinks that it was in this enormous pot that the great historian rid himself of the London soot, the great man and his situation become all the more evident. I looked up by chance and noticed on the wall the plaster mask that was made, it is said, at the moment of his death. That certainly is his face, I told myself. Yes, the face of the man who for forty years lay in this simple bed, contented himself with a "bath" consisting solely of this bowl of the same height as the cage structure for *kotatsu*, and who throughout his life never ceased to make his controversial observations. The lady guide's unstoppable outpourings gave me the impression of listening to somebody's telephoned greetings from Yokohama.

"Let us go up, shall we?" said the lady. Absorbed in my thoughts, detached from the world, far from the dust and noise of London, I felt I was seated alone at the top of a five-story pagoda. When the injunction "Let us go up" came again, I could not help showing my surprise. "What, is there another floor?" I found that strange. "Let us go up!" she repeated. I gave in to her persistence, thinking that the strange sensation that had come over me would simply become even more intense if I were to ascend still further towards the sky.

When I reached the third floor, without knowing why, I had a feeling of limitless joy or, rather, a strange and inexplicable sensation took hold of me. It was a loft. Raising one's eyes towards the ceiling, one noticed that it was low both on the left and right sides but raised in the middle. The shape was reminiscent of a horse's mane, and in the highest part of the ceiling the light came in through a glass pane. The rays all penetrated the attic in a straight line. Above my head, the immensity of the Heavens met the world through this one glass plate. There was nothing to obstruct the gaze—nothing at all. Carlyle had built this room at his own expense and had made it into his study, in which he shut himself off from the world. Once in this closed universe, he discovered the flaws in his plan: it is hot in summer and cold in winter, while in every season it is difficult to descend from it. There was a faint smile on the face of my guide, who turned towards me after having given her informative comments like a recitation learnt by heart. I nodded in silence.

Why was Carlyle obsessed with a desire to construct this room so close to the sky at such great expense? One need only read his writings to be convinced that he was a personality prone to flashes of temper. But it appears that his irascibility never left him any leisure to immerse himself in creation while remaining untouched by the many noises that invaded his surroundings. The sound of a piano, the barking of a dog, the crowing of a cock and squawking of a parrot all grated on his nerves, which were particularly sensitive. When he had reached the limit of his endurance, he aspired to create this room on the third floor, so far from men and so close to the sky.

In a letter addressed to Mrs Aitken, he expresses himself like this, "Disturbed by the various noises which penetrate through my window, which I have left open all through the summer, I explored every possible means of remedying this evil, but in vain. Everything proved useless and I noticed not the slightest improvement. After careful consideration I reached the conclusion that I would have to construct at the very top of the house a square measuring six by six meters with double walls and let the light and the air enter from overhead. This has now been achieved. Let the cocks of this vile world crow: I intend to be inconvenienced no longer."

The study was constructed according to plan from a sum equivalent to two thousand yen. It had the desired effect. At the same time, an unforeseen difficulty arose to assail the ears of our great man. It is true that neither the piano playing nor the barking of the dogs nor the crowing of the cock nor the squawking of the parrot were any longer noticeable. On the other hand, the church bells, the whistles of the trains and all the noises of this vile world reached him from afar like a curse and made heavy demands on his nervous system, just as in the past.

Noise. The noises that tormented Carlyle in England were the same as those that tormented Schopenhauer in Germany. Schopenhauer wrote, "Kant has published[66] a treatise on dynamics. I, however, write in order to toll the knell of energy. The noise made by something which one strikes, the noise of something rolling along everything comes from a misuse of the vital force. As for me, I simply feel torments day after day. My reasoning will make most people laugh, since when they hear noise they feel nothing. But if there are those in this world who are insensible to logic, indifferent to thought, to poetry and even to art, they are thus incapable of forgetting themselves, and there is no doubt that the failure of their mental system is the cause of the slowness of their comprehension." Carlyle and Schopenhauer are in truth two kindred nineteenth-century souls. It was at the moment when these thoughts came into my mind, that the good lady once again made her appearance and pressed me to go back downstairs.

Every story made me feel as if I were returning to the world below. It was as if the film of meditation in which I had hitherto been enfolded was little by little falling away. When I reached the bottom of the stairs, leant on the stair rail and looked out at the street, it

[66] An allusion to *Treatise on Main Strength: Thoughts on the True Estimation of Living Forces* (1746).

was as if I had suddenly once again become an ordinary human being. The spell was broken. My guide, indifferent, said, "Come and see the kitchen!" The kitchen was situated below street level. From where I was standing, I had to descend a further five or six steps. It was there that the good lady resided. One corner was occupied by a large stove. In her customary recitative tones, she told me, "On October 12th 1844 the famous poet Tennyson[67] visited Carlyle for the first time. They both sat down in front of this stove, stayed for two hours without saying a word, content to smoke." Was he who spent his days just under the roof, disgusted by noise, so much in love with silence that he wished to prolong it in a basement?

In conclusion, I was taken through the service door into the garden. I looked at the square, flat piece of ground and saw not a single tree worthy of the name, and no grass. According to my guide, there had been a time when one could pick cherries—and grapes as well. It would even seem that in one year Carlyle's wife gathered twenty-five sens' worth of nuts. She went on to say, "At the southeast end of the garden Carlyle's dog Nero is buried at a depth of about a meter. He died on February 1st 1860. At that time his grave bore a plaque, but this has unfortunately disappeared." My guide is without doubt well informed.

It was in this garden that Carlyle would wander in his nightshirt, his pipe in his mouth and wearing his

[67] Alfred Lord Tennyson (1802–92), English poet and playwright. When he was Poet Laureate, he became fascinated by the Arthurian legends, and adapted them to the Victorian framework. See *Idylls of the King* (1859–85). Among his best-known works are *Enoch Arden* (1864), *Maud* (1855) and *The Princess* (1847).

straw hat with a turned-up rim. In the height of summer, he put up a makeshift tent on the flagstones in
the shade, even adding a table, and plunged into the
task of setting down his ideas without allowing himself to be distracted. On one starlit evening, after
enjoying a final puff at his pipe, he lifted his eyes
heavenwards and cried, "Ah! Is it to be soon, the
moment when I shall see the sky for the last time? I
shall cease to see the world, this immense theater
born of the Creator's hand, this infinitude that I shall
no longer be able to touch. My efforts were not in
vain, my thirst for learning was sincere, and yet my
knowledge is but tiny!" Yes, it was in this garden that
Carlyle uttered these words.

To reward the good lady for her trouble, I placed
a coin in her hand. Her thanks again sounded recited.
An hour later, the London dust, the soot, the rumble
of the cabs and the Thames separated me from
Carlyle's house, which had become as distant as
another world.

27
The Diary of a Bicycle Rider
(Meiji 36)[68]

On a certain autumn day in the year 1902. At the window of the room in the boarding house[69] where I am staying, a white flag is displayed. This is the signal on which my landlady and I have agreed. Here she is embarking on the onerous task of conveying her twelve and a half stones up to the second floor. I should have been blunt or said nothing instead of expressing the action in such refined terms! Forty-two steps are required to reach the top. She stops twice on the way to catch her breath, and after three minutes and fifty seconds my august landlady's face appears in the doorway, wearing its characteristic sorrowful expression. The space around me suddenly contracts, the honor accorded me by her visit induces me to bend my shoulders, and she issues the order that has become the prime rule of our understanding, "Go cycling!"

Ah! What a sad business this bicycle tale is! I was to end by acknowledging defeat. Ill fate forced me to ride a bicycle as far as Lavender Hill. It would be more correct to say that I was forced to fall off a bicycle as far as that accursed spot! It was Mr ...[70] who,

[68] 1903.

[69] 81 The Chase, Clapham Common, London SW4. This was his fifth and last lodging in London. Opposite this house, at 80 The Chase, stands the Sōseki Museum.

[70] Inuzuka Takeo, who accompanied Ogasawara Nagayoshi to London. Lodging in the same boarding house as Sōseki, he had noticed the latter's depressed state and urged him to go cycling, at that time a very fashionable pastime in England.

combining the duties of teacher and instructor, and not withstanding my dejected demeanor, hauled me along to a cycle shop and chose a lady's bicycle, apparently from among those most suitable, saying that this one would serve the purpose. I asked the reason for his choice, to which he replied that nothing could be more in keeping with the insignificance of the first steps in my training. He no doubt assumed I had capitulated in advance and felt he was justified in uttering disparaging statements of this kind. For my part, while conceding my ignorance in the matter, I could not help finding it pitiful that a gentleman with a moustache should be forced to take exercise on a lady's bicycle, even if, as I admit, this moustache did not inspire respect. In short, I asked my instructor to begin my training on a normal bicycle, even if I were to fall off. Awaiting the reply in silence, I was ready, if I did not obtain satisfaction, to launch forth into an impassioned harangue extolling the heroism of a man who, constantly ready to face death, must not flinch from any danger. "Very well," he replied. "Let's have this one!" and he picked out a very ugly looking bicycle for a man.

I am well aware of the proverb which tells us that he whose handwriting is pleasing does not choose his brush. No matter! After all, since I am going to fall anyway, there is no point in worrying about the esthetics of the instrument, I told myself, laboriously pushing the selected bicycle along the road. On looking at it more closely, I noticed that all the "joints" were loose. I was thus obliged to mount a rusty vehicle! In other words, I had crossed the ocean from the other side of the world specially for the purpose of getting up on to this old bike! I asked the dealer whether there was no age limit for a bicycle and angrily exclaimed that this object ought to have been retired donkey's years ago, to live out its tranquil days by the side of the sheds. How downcast it must have felt—incidentally, it was complaining audibly— at the idea of having to end its life being dragged along by a lonely gentleman from Asia to whose orders it was compelled to submit! At least leave it at liberty to give expression to its resentment by the grating of its old bones! As regards the rider in question, whose sole wish was to finish it off before even getting on it, he nervously grasped the handlebars, gave the bicycle a push, tried to take off.... Anybody witnessing the difficulties, which it cost him the greatest effort to overcome before he had even mounted the saddle, must surely have wept at the thought of what would happen once he was up!

"Where are we going?"

"How do you mean 'where'? To somewhere there are not many people, of course, as it's the first time! I must be able to fall off without being a general laughing stock, it seems to me." It is a strange thing that someone who has given in should be able to dictate his terms. The magnanimity and compassion of the competent authority cause it to be sorry for me and take me towards the ride by the side of Clapham Common, where at first sight there seemed to be no witnesses. Once we had arrived, I was told, "Well try getting on, then!" This time there was no going back. My hair, caused to bristle by my anger at receiving this absurd order, rose up to meet the inside of the top of my protective helmet. At the same moment, I cried out for help.

For after all, the expression "Get on!" does not form part of my vocabulary. Formerly, when I was still in my own country and enviably situated, I had never had to attempt to mount unaided. Until that day when I lost everything, after having crossed the seas ... consequently, this injunction "Get on!" seemed to me to be far too sadly lacking in charity to one's fellow being. However, I complied with the order despite its cruelty, adjusting my helmet more firmly on my head and seizing the handlebars. Thus attired, the warrior must have presented a proud spectacle, until he was in the saddle (which, you will agree, was proof of additional courage on his part), for at the decisive moment, as might have been expected, I fell, although the bicycle, exhibiting exemplary calm, did not turn round or make any movement at all. As for its rider, ejected from the saddle, he could only feel astonishment at such confirmation of his instructor's precepts, which he had initially doubted.

The trainer declared, "It's a mistake to start by settling yourself firmly in the saddle. You shouldn't put your feet on the pedals either. If you manage to make the wheels perform a complete revolution simply by clinging to the machine, that's good enough!" What an infinity of desolation was embodied in those words!

It was in vain that I clung on to it. The wheels did not even turn halfway round. I emitted a variety of exclamations and silently appealed for help. The result was as expected. My instructor came over to me and said, "Come along, I'll hold you firmly. Get up!" But no sooner was I on the saddle than I was back on the ground. "I told you so. You bent your knees! This time you are going to seat yourself gently on the saddle and hold the handlebars with both hands. All right? Are you ready? I'll give the machine a push. Take hold of it while moving, and start pedaling!" So there was the learner, trembling with fear, being pushed forward. Just when everything was in place and the movement had been started, something happened which was not allowed for—a fall on to the gravel. Who but God could have foreseen it? Extreme stupefaction took possession of me.

A few passersby had stopped to look. Others continued on their way with a mocking laugh. On the other side, at the foot of an oak tree, a children's nurse was leaning against a seat and had for a little while been staring fixedly at me. I did not know what she found to look at like this, but I suspected that she was unable to tear her eyes away from the perspiring and bleeding man on the ground, still struggling wildly. Thus exposed to admiring glances, I could only ignore the two or three scratches inflicted on my shins, and I called upon my instructor to "let me have another go". "Give me a good push. What? I shall be on the ground again? That's quite possible, but after all it's my body!" I had completely forgotten my defeat. I took a deep breath. Suddenly, at a moment when I least expected it, someone behind me called out, "Sir!" In some surprise, my contacts with the inhabitants of this country being rare, I turned round and found myself facing a policeman, standing very erect and capable of putting respectable people out of countenance. I am not among those who come up against such people. As for him, he gave the impression of having approached this ignoramus for a compelling reason; that is, because I was on a path reserved for horsemen, so that, if I wanted to ride a bicycle, I had to use the ordinary roadway. I submitted in a language in which colloquial English was mixed with a Japanese marked by classical courtesy, after which, having thus demonstrated the level of my erudition, I appealed to my instructor, who, thinking that to each day is sufficient the evil thereof, suggested that we should go home. We thus set off on the homeward journey, I wheeling my bicycle, as I could no longer mount it. "How did it go?" asked my landlady doubtfully. I felt the breath of defeat. The vehicle creaked where it lay, evening fell, and my ears were buzzing. Ah, autumn was arriving!

On a certain day of a certain month.

Standing at the top of the hill, the famous bicycle by my side, I prudently waited while calmly looking down for the signal from my instructor, and filled with a secret ambition to descend all in one go this slope of no doubt over a hundred meters with a gradient of about one in five and a width of over twenty meters. It was a sparsely frequented spot bordered by imposing residences. It did not so far seem clear whether the British Government had instructed the public works authorities to build this thoroughfare on learning that a gentleman who had arrived from Asia intended to come here and practice falling off a bicycle. At all events, it was an ideal spot for a cycle path whether the policeman's rebuke had given my instructor a fright or whether he just wanted to save himself the trouble of pushing my bicycle. After the previous evening, he took me to places where man and machine could move free of care.

After having calculated that nobody would come on the scene and that the spot was not frequented by any cabs, my mentor said, "Come on, this is the right moment. Hurry up and get on!" I should like to remark in passing that neither he nor I had yet used the verb "mount" in its customary sense. In my vocabulary, this word means to seat oneself on the saddle with one's feet on the pedals, placing one's

trust in the principle of dynamics by which the movement occurs without any demands being made on
the human will, without the need to avoid people or
horses and without having to hang back before water
or fire and with the sole task of proceeding straight
to the selected goal. I suddenly curled up with the
stomachache I used to experience when attending
the aerobatics performed for the New Year's Day
festivities by the military firemen on great bamboo
ladders. I really do wonder whether I am entitled to
use that word. Well, to be brief, since I had to get on,
on I got, finding myself stuck to the bicycle and glued
to its saddle, as it were—a perfect communion
between the man and his machine! So there I was,
whizzing down the slope like the west wind. Funnily
enough, some wag, in admiration of my cycling activity, started to applaud from the window of a proper-
ty on the left. Before I had even had time to feel surprised, I had already started on the second half of my
descent. This time a terrible encounter fell to my lot.
About fifty schoolgirls were moving towards me in a
line. For all that I was in the presence of females, it
was impossible for me to cut a proud figure. With
both hands engaged, my back bent and my right leg
waving in the air, I tried to alight, but the machine
would not obey me. It was a desperate situation. All I
could do was continue on my headlong route with a
style which was not mine. I passed by the side of the
crowd of feminine creatures, and the machine, without even leaving me time to give a sigh of relief, had
now reached the bottom and was continuing along
level ground without the slightest sign of being about
to stop. It continued on its way without changing
speed and took the direction of the crossroads,
where there was a policeman on duty. I panicked at

the prospect of further reprimands but found it impossible to call a halt to my acrobatics. The bicycle, apparently asking me to enter into a suicide pact for love, continued on its mad journey, finally forsaking the roadway for the pavement, but without coming to a stop, hit a wall and turned over, landing less than a yard from the officer, who said with a smile, "That run must have done for you!" I simply replied, "Yes!"

Another day of a certain month.

"Do you go to the British Museum to carry out your research?"

"No, I hardly ever go there, because I have a habit of making notes in the books I read."

"Oh, really? In that case, it is better for you to have your own books, since you are then at liberty to use them as you wish. As for me, that is where I go if I want to refer to a work...."

Sitting slightly further back, the wife opens her mouth to say, "Mr Natsume, you study very keenly, I believe, do you not?"

"No, it is some time since I did any studying to speak of, because on somebody's advice I have become a cycling fan, and that is all I do from morning till evening."

"That is most pleasant, do you not think so? Do you know that everybody in the household can ride a bicycle? No doubt you, too, are able to cycle long distances!"

Your humble servant, thus crowned with an unearned halo, who was ignorant of the very meaning of the expression "ride a bicycle", and whose talent consisted solely of being able to come down a hill on to which he had been hoisted, agonized at the words "cycle long distances". But in this twentieth century, which has developed to such an extent that exaggeration has become second nature to it, I assumed the detached air of the man who knows what he is about and let fall the remark, "True. Although I'd be lying if I claimed that I toured for any great distance, I love coming down the hills I have gone up, and I must confess that it is quite pleasant to get down off the saddle!"

The young girl, who until then had kept silent, seemed to mistake my meaning and turned to her parents as if to ask for their consent. "What do you say to our all going together to Wimbledon with Mr Natsume one of these days?" Her father and mother together turned towards me and looked at me. I was overcome with embarrassment and twisted about on my chair. I found it impossible to decline the invitation of such a beautiful girl, and a civilized man cannot permit himself to forfeit a lady's consideration without incurring lifelong dishonor. Forced to say something, I tried to swallow but was prevented from doing so by my detachable collar, several centimeters high, that imprisoned my throat. I nevertheless succeeded in uttering, in both relaxed and pleased tones, "That would be simply delightful, but...."

"You are certainly very busy with your work, but perhaps you would be free next Saturday, for instance?" The tone became increasingly pressing. I once again said "But..." while telling myself that this conjunction did not necessarily have to be followed by any further words. I nevertheless remained perplexed, wondering why I had used this word. My reflections were forestalled by the statement with which I myself continued my declaration, "But I am afraid the place is too crowded, because ... well, I have not yet had much practice!" Thus I myself supplied the means for my defeat.

"Don't worry! The roads down there couldn't be quieter!" The trap closed on me, and there was no going back. "Well, well, it's exactly like when I'm perched on my saddle!" I remarked to myself with an astonishment tinged with admiration. This understandable feeling, however, did not lead to any firm conclusion, and, finding myself with my back to the wall, I repeated "But..." and followed it with "But will the weather be good on Saturday?" Finding myself driven into a corner, I made one last attempt. Fool that I was! Who could answer such a question? This was the moment for my capitulation. The master, acting as judge, opened his mouth and pronounced sentence: "There is no need to fix a definite date. I will come and fetch you one of these days on my bike and we will go for a spin together." What was there to say? Had I heard correctly? Going for a spin with a cyclist like me! It was proof that he had, as it were, issued me my cyclist's diploma! In the end, I did not go with the pretty girl to Wimbledon. Was that a piece of good luck or a misfortune for me? This question was on my mind for over forty-eight hours without my being able to come to any precise conclusion. It is what the Circle of Poets for the Revival of the Haiku[71] would call "artistic blur".

Another day of a certain month.

After several days' painful detailed cogitation, I reached the following conclusion: a bicycle is not equipped with a saddle and pedals just to make a good impression. The saddle is there to sit on and the pedals are designed to rotate according to the

[71] From 1893 onwards, the *haiku* of the school directed by Masaoka Shiki appeared in a column of the paper *Nihon*.

pressure applied by the rider's feet. As regards the handlebars, these are the most dangerous instrument of all, fascinating you and, after having cast their spell on you, causing you to perform senseless movements.

I who aspire to take the "Cycle Road"[72] across Clapham Common holding my "mount" by its "bridle" and accompanied by my instructor, whom I have already mentioned, and by his friend, His Excellency the Count of....[73] Picture the scene. We were about to enter an avenue used by horse-drawn trams. In between my two companions, I had no freedom to guide my "steed" as I would have wished. Confident that I would be able to continue forward, I fixed my attention on a convenient corner. At the very moment when I was preparing to cross over, an unexpected cart arrived on my right without any warning, passing in front of my nose without a single word of apology. If I adopted the attitude which I had always used to this day, all I had to do was to press forward, but my principle is only to attack if certain of victory. If it is perfectly obvious that defeat is certain, I am bound by tradition to abide by the relevant clause of the family constitution, which stipulates that any collision is to be avoided, particularly one between a creaking, squeaking bicycle like mine and an enormous cart. I had to remember the pieces of advice left by my father in his will and avoid accidents at any cost. All right, the question was this: whether I were to go to the left or to the right, one of

---

[72] The term used is *satori* ("the awakening"), borrowed by Sōseki from Zen terminology.

[73] This refers to Ogasawara Nagayoshi (1885–1935), a politician who became a member of the House of Lords in 1918. He studied at Cambridge for three years.

my companions would inevitably fall. Which would I choose? The Count's son or my respected instructor? A cruel dilemma! Why are we insignificant beings forced to commit such outrages? No freedom was left to me. I was imprisoned between my two companions. If I chose the one on the right as my victim, I committed an outrage against nobility. If I chose the one on the left, it was the respect due to the master that I trampled underfoot. I thus had only two alternatives—to retreat or to fall. I reflected. The calculation was made very rapidly, since up to then I had never experienced panic at the critical moment of decision. If I had been able to retreat, it would not have been a bad choice; at all events it would have been preferable to falling. Alas, we have not yet progressed to bicycles with handlebars at the back! "Devil take it!" I told myself, "Take your courage in both hands and fall!" And I fell heavily between the bicycles of my two fellow cyclists. Three or four yards from the scene of my intrepid act there stood a policeman with boredom depicted on his countenance. He looked like ... how should I put it? ... Yes, he was just like the decoration that usually accompanies the *sashimi*.[74] The decoration let out a triple laugh: ha, ha, ha! This laugh was neither sarcastic nor frigid nor lighthearted. Nor did it burst forth. No, it was, strictly speaking, an artificial laugh, just as if it had been emitted to order. I wondered whether the policeman had been paid sixpence or a shilling for his laugh but am to this day ignorant of the precise amount of his reward.

To the devil with the policeman and his laugh! I hurried off and got up in pursuit of my companions.

[74] Sliced raw fish.

As to whether I should have done the same if in place of the policeman it had been the young lady of the other day.... It is impossible to reply in the abstract to such a question, and I prefer not to ask it. I will therefore continue my narrative.

On the pretext that they could not guide me over strange territory, my companions instructed me to go in front of them—me, completely devoid of self-assurance! True, I might be capable of leading them, but I was ignorant of the art of riding a bicycle. I could not go where I wanted to go, as it was my bicycle that chose to turn in the direction it found most convenient. We thus found ourselves in the same place, turning round and round. At first I made an effort to put them off, but I could not get them to be patient any longer. This time a decision was taken to go in another direction. It was in vain that I had given my consent. I did not succeed in turning in the direction required. The things of this world do not obey us.... Just as I had crossed two-thirds of the road to be negotiated, I straightened the handlebars with a desperate effort. The bicycle suddenly turned through an angle of ninety degrees. What was the outcome of this unexpected exploit? The story is not sufficiently interesting to be worth the trouble of keeping you on tenderhooks, so I will tell it without keeping you waiting. Up to then, I had not paid attention, but there was another cyclist who, owing to my sudden turn, was just behind me. Taken by surprise by my "volte-face", he found himself on the ground, not having had time to move to one side. As I learned later, when one wishes to make a turn at a cross-roads, one rings the bell of one's bicycle or puts out one's hand; in short, it is good form to give warning. I, who like the unexpected, was unfamiliar with this everyday rule of good breeding. Besides which, how could you expect me to ring the bell or raise my hand? No margin was left to me to perform these tiresome maneuvers. To turn suddenly without giving any warning was the only action left open to me. Just as it was perfectly understandable that the man traveling in my wake should fall as a result of being taken by surprise, there was nothing surprising in our both having done what was natural for us to do. But it would seem that Westerners' logic has not advanced this far. Exploding and foaming with rage, the man on the ground was abusing me and calling me a "Chink".[75] I should have been entitled to pay him back in kind, but here my fundamentally chivalrous nature came to the fore. Remarking "I am so sorry!" I took the turning without looking back. The fact is that by the time I had made up my mind to look back, my victim's bicycle had already overtaken me. All I had been able to say was "I am so sorry!" With my candid nature, I should have a bad conscience were I to make myself out to be a hero, and this is why I have recounted the incident in such detail. And if you chance to form too high an opinion of my heroism, it is by no means impossible that I shall resent this in you throughout my seven lives to come!

Another day of a certain month.

I tried to overcome my discouragement by telling myself that the fate of man and of things is enforceable, since the bicycle of Sōseki had caused someone to fall when he was expecting to fall himself. Today, eminently self-satisfied, I hurried towards Battersea

---

[75] The author, in fact, used the expression "Chin-chin-Chinaman". "Chin-chin" comes from the Chinese term *ts'ing-ts'ing*, a polite way of greeting and addressing someone, which contrasts with "Chinaman", a pejorative term.

Park. This is as quiet a spot as could be, but before one gets there one has to negotiate three very busy thoroughfares which, for a learned man in embryo such as I, are insuperable. After having ascended Lavender Hill, I traveled as far as the middle of the crossroads. On the other side stood a horse-drawn tramcar facing me, while on the right, facing in the opposite direction, stood an enormous cart. There was a gap of a little over a yard between the two vehicles. I rode my machine into this gap. Just as my wheel came level with the horse's front legs, that is to say, when my body was between the tram and the cart, a bicycle came at breakneck speed from the opposite direction. As life is the most important thing in urgent situations of this kind, I felt I had no time to decide whether to go back or to drop. So I dropped, clumsily, holding on to the animal's side with my left hand, thanks to which I succeeded in avoiding a highly inelegant fall on to my belly. My relief was shortlived: the tram was set in motion! The bolting horse flung my bicycle up into the air. As for the cyclist, he passed by us with an air of indifference. An immeasurably depressing scene.... At that moment, winding his way along in a cabriolet, a grand-looking gentleman at my rear, brandishing his whip, shouted, "Everything's all right. You're not going to be killed, don't worry!" Stupefied, I murmured to myself, "Is it possible that they get people to ride bicycles in order to kill them? England's certainly a fearful place!"

****

Since when, submitting to my twelve and a half stone landlady's injunctions to go cycling, I have suffered five serious falls. As for the others, I had better not try to count them. Once I injured my knee by running into a wall. Another time my nails were torn out through a collision with a tree, and I will pass over the remaining examples. If I had at least achieved some result as the outcome of this bitter struggle— but it was in vain. The good woman of twelve and a half stone tirelessly makes fun of people. At any ironic remark made to me, her sister, who is only half her weight, treats my yellow face to an unblinking stare and devotes herself without concealment to her task of ascertaining whether there is the tiniest change to be observed in my physiognomy. What constancy and determination in the performance of duty! Since I have been the object of these two ladies' attention, I have become more and more suspicious, my feeling like those of a child ill-treated by its stepmother has become constantly intensified, and in the end I closed the door which I had left ajar. I have shut myself away, and the yellowish shade of my face simply deepens. The two women have made it their daily task to verify the brightening of my complexion, which for them does duty as a barometer. I sometimes wonder what I have gained by submitting to their will in this manner: nothing but eating two boarders' share while wasting precious study time. In short, if my gain has been nil, I believe the two good women likewise failed to profit in any way. Life is very cruel.

28
Sōseki's Letters
from London

To Kyō,[76]

London, January 22nd 1901, evening
6, Flodden Road, Camberwell New Road, London S.E.

I am constantly anxious, wondering how you spend the day. I expect everyone is well? Baby must have arrived by now, and I hope all went well. As for me, I am in good health and am devoting all my time to assiduous study. So do not worry, and look after yourself, because the postnatal period calls for special care. Winter here is hard to bear. When there is a thick fog, everything becomes invisible, as in a night without a moon, and I have a very unpleasant feeling. I long to return to Japan and feel the rhythm of the seasons and once again enjoy the beautiful days radiant with light. There are many Japanese here, but I should waste a lot of money and time if I were with them. I therefore concentrate on reading as much as possible. Fortunately, I have not caught a single cold since I arrived. However, the state of my stomach is not satisfactory, although it is nothing serious. All I hope is that I shall not fall ill during my stay here.

London is a city that offers all kinds of temptations, and whenever I go for a walk I discover things that I would like to bring back as souvenirs. But my resources are very limited. I cannot buy anything,

[76] Sōseki married Nakane Kyōko, daughter of a high-ranking official, on June 9th 1896.

and I make a point of taking my walks a good distance from these riches.

Would you please send me the photograph taken of you with Fude in your arms last year when we were in Kumamoto? You only need to put it between two sheets of paper, putting a piece of thread round them to keep them together, then send it to me by post. One cannot have a photograph taken of oneself here for less than ten yen. It will be a long time before I shall be able to send you one.

In Japan, like anywhere else, it is difficult to live alone. All the more so in England, where the customs and habits are different. It really afflicts one. In the morning, when I get up, I have a rubdown in cold water, shave and comb my hair, and that is all. However, this still takes a long time. When I dress or undress, I have to struggle with the shirt buttons, and find this task in itself a strain. I do not have much occasion to mix with Westerners. Anyway, how could I do so, with no money and no spare time?

If things are dear here, they appear on the other hand to be made to last. Men's clothes, in particular, are of better quality than in Paris and are really fine. I have had a frock coat and a suit made, but as I went to a tailor a long way from the good-class neighborhoods, it goes without saying that it is all of mediocre quality. The frock coat, furthermore, is a failure. I used the very little money I had left over after the voyage. Result: the cuffs of the frock coat are too wide and the sleeves of the overcoat are too narrow. So I am in real trouble! The Japanese who have been here three or four months longer than the others think they know everything about London and make fun of the newcomers' clothes. Their own are certainly strange, but they flaunt them, cheated by their tailor, who has charged them exorbitant sums. They imagine that because they have paid high prices, the fabric and the cut are infinitely superior to other people's. The fools!

You can easily imagine how expensive life is here when I tell you that a pair of shoes costs about ten yen. On the other hand, knitted woolens are comparatively cheap. The collars are immaculate, white and very hard, and cannot be compared to those one finds in Japan. If I go out for lunch, the simplest dish costs sixty or seventy sen right away. What we can buy with a yen at home costs ten times as much here. The consequence is that, little by little, without noticing it, one gets into self-indulgent habits. It is not surprising that the Japanese who come home after studying abroad are criticized for being spendthrift. If in Japan you do what here would be considered quite modest, that alone is enough to gain a reputation for extravagance. Just imagine it!

Despite the biting cold, the climate is on the whole easier to bear than in Tokyo. For the last two or three days, it has been just like spring. I do not know whether this is exceptional or whether it is the same every year at this time. I expect it is cold in Tokyo, too. The year has just started, but to me it does not feel like the New Year at all.

I have been to the theater three or four times. The splendor of the auditorium all upholstered in red velvet simply dazzled me. Everything, including the décor and the costumes, was beautiful to look at. I was particularly impressed by a performance in which about fifty girls in rows, clothed in gauzy dresses, divided up the scene into squares as they danced. I should like to be able to show all of you this magnificent sight! In the course of the performance, some of the dancers were lifted off the floor (by a system of wires) and flew airily away. The little lamps ornamenting their hair, hands and bosoms lit up at the same time. These lights enhanced the brightness of the jewelry which they wore. I am sure that if you just imagine these thousand lights, this will be enough to give you an idea of the magnificence of the spectacle. Only to be able to attend the performance under favorable conditions one has to be in evening dress! It goes without staying that smoking is forbidden and that one feels awkward. As for me, I was highly embarrassed, having made my way into the theater in a lounge suit and brown shoes!

In this country, tradesmen of superior status normally wear a great coat and sport a top hat. Some of them give the impression of having obtained their hats and threadbare coats from a rag picker: they remind me of *rōnin*[77] in the depths of poverty. Men's clothes are sober. I see a lot of black jackets, and if the trousers are striped they are of such a dull color that if you viewed them from a distance you would take them for plain trousers. This is all one sees. People of below average means wear only plain shades, summer and winter. Those who belong to a higher social class change their clothes in the evening without fail, putting on evening wear for dinner. The evening suit is obligatory at this hour. As regards funerals or weddings, most people attend them in frock coats. As for the Japanese, whether they are in dinner jackets or in frock coats, they cut no figure at all. While I was still in Japan, I was not

[77] A term used both for peasants unable to pay their dues and obliged to flee from their village and for *samurai* who had lost their lord and were thus left without means.

conscious of the color of our skin, but since I have been here I have fretted at finding myself so yellow. Furthermore, I am small. I have not yet met anyone smaller than me. Nor am I broad shouldered. When I think to myself, "Look, there's a funny person coming towards me!" it's my own reflection that I see in the mirror. It is something that I experience quite frequently. I can put up with being unable to do anything about the shape of my face—but my size! I wish I were taller. I assume that children must be made to sit on a chair from their earliest years. Most of the people here inexplicably have something remarkable about them. I feel helpless at the idea that if I spent ten years of my life in this country it would be in vain. I should not grow any bigger. When it falls to my lot to see an Occidental smaller than me, it gives me pleasure, but on the whole even the women are taller than me! It never ceases to amaze me.

It is already unpleasant enough to live in an environment to which one is not accustomed, and as I have no money I feel my powerlessness all the more keenly. I shut myself away in my boarding house as in a besieged castle, and my only resource is to study, because I am afraid that if I go out I shall spend money.

I am sure Fude has grown a lot and I should like you to give some news of her. She will be starting to walk by now, and I hope you will be very careful to see she does not knock against any dangerous objects.

I have not yet written to Suzuki Jun once. Give him my best regards when you get a chance.

I should like to write to you more often, but that would take up more of my precious time. I hope you will understand and will not hold it against me. Send your letters to the Legation, because it is by no means certain that there will be no change of address, even if I have no intention of moving for the moment. Takahama[78] has sent me three issues of *Hototogisu*[79] since I have been here.

When you have recovered from your confinement, have a false tooth put in. If you have not enough money for it, ask your father. I will pay him back on my return. I advise you not to fix your hair. It is better, both for the hair and for the brain, not to do so. There is a fluid called "water of quinine". It is a remedy which stops dandruff from forming. Try applying some of this. Perhaps it will stop you from losing your hair.

If I write too much I shall lose time. So I will stop here.

Kinnosuke[80]

P.S.
The day for sending mail has been fixed. Ask the post

[78] Takahama Kyoshi (1874–1959), a poet and friend of Sōseki who managed the literary journal *Hototogisu*.
[79] A journal with an emphasis on poetry (*haiku*) created in 1897. It was in this journal that Sōseki's novel *Wagahai wa Neko de aru* (I am a Cat) appeared in 1905.
[80] The author's legal name is Kinnosuke Natsume. He adopted the nom de plume of Sōseki. This name is made up of two *kanji* (Chinese characters) which form part of the expression Sōseki Chinryu. The literal meaning of this is "Take a stone for your pillow and the current to rinse your mouth", a kind of maxim which evokes a life free from all restraint and involvement. The Chinese in olden times used it and it was they who inverted the terms by mistake, resulting in "Rinse your mouth with a stone and take the current for a pillow". This expression has been transmitted in its incorrect form and denotes the obstinacy of somebody unwilling to admit defeat.

office for the calendar of dates planned for this year. You will find it gives the names of the ships which sail for England via America or India, as well as the day and the month. You should be able to get these details from the post office or somewhere. The mail sent via America arrives about two weeks earlier than the other mail. All you need do is put "via America" in the top left-hand corner of the envelope.

To Kyō
London, Friday, March 8th 1901
6, Flodden Road, Camberwell New Road, London S.E

I was expecting to receive mail from Japan, but not a single line has arrived. The "Rio de Janeiro", which set sail from Yokohama on February 2nd, has been wrecked off San Francisco, and I am very worried as to whether there was mail for me on that very boat.

Has Baby arrived? Is it a boy or a girl?[81] I know absolutely nothing, and you must understand how quickly one gets worried in a far country. If you are unable to write yourself, why do you not ask your father or somebody else? If that is impossible, you need only ask Tsuchiya or Yuasa.

I had also asked you to send me the newspaper, but nothing comes—nothing at all. If there are material reasons that prevent you from doing so, I will put up with it, but I cannot accept your leaving me in ignorance of everything!

As for me, I am busy as usual, and however much I want to write long letters I cannot do so. I count on

[81] A girl, Tsune, was born on January 26th 1901.

you to convey my greetings to everybody.

I go to the theater now and again as part of my training. It is truly magnificent and leaves me spellbound. Yesterday, for instance, I went to a London theater which resembles the Kabukiza[82] and is called Drury Lane. I was amazed. It must be said that this *kyōgen*[83] was not a play in the strict sense. It is called "pantomime".[84] The main purpose of the performance is to exhibit the stage effects and the costumes, which are magnificent. These perform-ances are chiefly intended for the Christmas period, but as they are highly successful they have been put on since last year continuously. (London, being a big city, the theatrical performances are too many to count, and when the play is a success it may be performed continuously for three whole years. When I tell you that they still never play to an empty house, you will agree with me that it is a very mysterious phenomenon.) I cannot describe the beauty of the stage effects. About fifty girls resembling the *tennin*[85] sculpted in relief on the Temple of Kannon[86] execute dances in a submarine palace, providing the basic scene. At a certain moment, a further group of about fifty dancers comes across the floor of the stage, which is suddenly plunged into darkness. A moment

[82] A theater built in 1889 in Tokyo, near Ginza.
[83] A traditional theatrical form which goes back to the Muromachi period (1336–1576).
[84] This refers to Charles Perrault's tale *The Sleeping Beauty*.
[85] A Buddhist term for celestial beings of feminine form, illustrated jumping in the air and playing music.
[86] A sanctuary dedicated to Kannon (feminine illustration of one of the most popular bodhisattvas of Buddhism), the main building of the Sensōji Temple, situated in the Asakusa district of Tokyo. Built in 1849, it has been classified as a national monument. The *tennin* which can be viewed there are the work of the painter Dōmoto Insho.

later, the scene has changed and from the center of the stage a jet of water gushes forth—at first violet-colored, the next yellow, then red, then blue. Then up rises a palace mottled in gold and silver, on which the columns and interior all light up and shine like diamonds. The dancers' hair and costumes light up and sparkle with a thousand little red bulbs. Do not imagine that one is able to witness these wonders only in the first act or only in the second! No, the changes of scene succeed one another throughout the whole program, and it is a spectacle that would be impossible to provide without spending a fortune. Try to imagine a mixture of heavenly moving pictures and of rotating magic lanterns. Just think! You have only just been looking at a palace beneath the ocean, and already it is covered over by the wonderful flower garden which succeeds it, and after this it is the sun shining on the sea, while finally we find blue-tinged mountains appearing and then turning into a snow-clad landscape. It affords intense pleasure to the eyes.

As for me, I am in good health. I seem to have put on weight. I am in a hurry to come back to Japan. I will tell you the rest another time.

Kinnnosuke

Letter to Masaoka Shiki

London, Wednesday, December 18th 1901
(c/o. Miss Leale, 81 The Chase, Clapham Common,
London S.W.)

It is impossible to go for a walk in a place like Hyde Park on a Sunday without coming across orators delivering speeches on the public highway. Here we have the hoarse voice of a Professor Amen calling upon Jesus Christ—and there, only a few meters away, we hear the vituperations of an unbeliever: "Hell? But what is Hell? If those who do not believe in God go to Hell, then Voltaire is sure to be there, and Ingersoll too. I think Hell is full of geniuses and is infinitely preferable to Heaven crawling with imbeciles!" This is a far more fiery and convincing tone than my own pitiful discourses dotted with hesitations! No adjective would suffice to express the persuasive force exuded by the raucous outpourings of the speaker. On the opposite side to the freethinker, a man holds aloft the banner of philanthropy and takes himself for Auguste Comte. To one side of him, a speaker is furiously opposing the theories of Huxley. A little way to the rear, a stunted-looking man cries in a loud voice totally out of keeping with his faded appearance, "Listen to me, everyone! Last year in Japan I met the celebrated Marquis Ito (he was referring to Itō Hirobumi),[87] whom in a completely private conversation I was able to question on religion." And further tall stories of the same kind.

---

[87] Itō Hirobumi (1841–1909), the most influential politician in the Meiji government, under whose auspices the Japanese constitution, in force until 1945, was established. It was he who developed the principle of the annexation of Korea by Japan. He was assassinated in Harbin by a Korean in 1909.

The other day there was a judo and wrestling tournament in St James Hall. There was a prize of two hundred and fifty yen for the victor! You can well imagine that I made a point of going! The fifty-sen seats were sold out. I managed to get in for one yen twenty-five sen, but it is the same here as in the *sumō*[88] halls in Japan: it is impossible to make out the contestants' faces! Unless one spends five or six yen, one has to forgo any seat from where it would be possible to distinguish the expressions. You will agree that this is rather dear for what one could call "blind seats". As for me, since it was *sumō* I resigned myself to it. Having said this, I am convinced that if I had gone in the hope of seeing pretty women, I should have asked for a refund and left on the spot! But let us leave aside the sordid aspect and deal with the essential matter, that is to say, the victory. Was it the Japanese wrestler or the English wrestler who was defeated? It would be very difficult for me to tell you, because in the end the contest did not take place, apparently owing to lack of time! On the other hand, I was able to see the contest between the Swiss and the English champion. Well, you know, *sumō* fought the Western way is just a great joke! Whether one falls on one's knees, one's side or flat on one's back, one is not "given out" until one has stayed down, with both one's shoulders touching the floor, while the referee counts the seconds! You can imagine that it is no easy matter to decide the victory. Every contestant tries to knock his adversary over by jumping on his back, while on all fours he acts like a frog, trying all the time, needless to say, to avoid being

[88] A form of wrestling with two contestants seated and facing each other, their "holds" being confined to the upper part of the body.

thrown. They look as if they are playing "seated sumō". Result: it went on until midnight! That will show you what an exceptional match it was! You can imagine my surprise on reading an article in the next morning's paper which described the match in question and duly gave you an idea of how seriously the press here takes its work.

Just think, I have moved again![89] Seven times in thirty-five years, in a search for quietness, I have changed my address, but it has always been in vain. This is certainly nothing to boast about! For my part, I have already moved from one boarding house to another five times since I came to England! The place where I am now is inhabited by two ladies and a retired army captain. It is rather as if I had been deported to the Kingdom of Old. Yes, I have become an inhabitant of the Island of the Aged. The landlady reads Milton and Shakespeare. In addition, she speaks fluent French. I am overcome with humility. "Mr Natsume," she sometimes asks me, "do you know the origin of this verse?" From time to time, she pays me compliments. "Your English is excellent. You will certainly have started learning it at a very young age?" She probably knows, however, that this is by no means the case. I feel like asking her to stop making fun of me. Since I have been here, I have learned that receiving compliments is a thing to be feared. The men are not so bad, but the women exclaim "Wonderful!" at the slightest trifle. "Is it so wonderful to speak as badly as I do?" I sometimes ask, not without irony, hoping thereby to put a stop

[89]Sōseki's last London address, the boarding house kept by Elizabeth and Priscilla Leale at 81 The Chase, London SW4, where the writer took up residence from July 20th 1901 to December 4th 1902.

to this shower of flatteries. A thick fog is pressing against my windowpane. It is dark in my study, even though the hands of the clock point to an hour of the afternoon. I feel a gnawing hunger. Upon these highly philosophical considerations I shall lay down my pen and go to lunch.

Titles by Sōseki Natsume

Inside My Glass Doors

Translated by Sammy I. Tsunematsu

ISBN 0-8048-3312-5

Originally published in daily serialization in the *Asahi* newspaper in 1915, *Inside My Glass Doors* is a collection of thirty-nine autobiographical essays penned a year before the author's death in 1916. Written in the genre of *shōhin* ("little items"), the personal vignettes provide a kaleidoscopic view of Sōseki Natsume's private world. The story is filled with flashbacks to Sōseki's youth—his classmates, family, and old neighborhood—as well as episodes from the more recent past and his observations on the state of the world.

The 210th Day

Translated by Sammy I. Tsunematsu

ISBN 0-8048-3320-6

The 210th Day, first published in 1906, is written almost entirely in dialogue form. It focuses on two friends, Kei and Roku, as they attempt to climb the rumbling Mount Aso as it threatens to erupt. During their progress up the mountain and during a stopover at an inn, Roku banters with Kei about his background, behavior and reaction to the things they see along the way. The book reveals both Sōseki's gift for the striking image and his talent for combining Western autobiography and the Japanese traditional literary diary.

Spring Miscellany and London Essays

Translated by Sammy I. Tsunematsu

ISBN 0-8048-3326-5

First published in serial form in the *Asahi* newspaper in 1909, *Spring Miscellany* is an eclectic pastiche—a literary miscellany—of twenty-five sketches, heir to the great *zuihitsu* tradition of discursive prose. These personal vignettes, which reveal Sōseki's interest in authentic, unadorned self-expression, are clearly auto-biographical and reveal his kaleidoscopic view of his private world. There are scattered episodes from his youth and from the more recent past. Of particular interest are the accounts of his stay in England between 1900 and 1902 as well as letters he wrote at the time.

The Wayfarer

Translated by Beongcheon Yu

ISBN 4-8053-0204-6

Written in the years 1912–13, *The Wayfarer* explores the moral dilemma of individuals caught in the violent transition of Japan from feudal to modern society The protagonist Ichiro is caught in a triangle with his wife Onao and his brother Jiro. What ensues is, in a sense, a battle of the sexes between a couple forced to live together by tradition, a constant duel of two minds which allows for no finality. Ichiro's plight is not only the plight of the modern intellect, and modern man in general, but of the predicament of modern man in isolation from his family, society and culture.

Grass on the Wayside

Translated by Edwin McClellan

ISBN 4-8053-0258-5

Completed in 1915 during a period of rapidly declining health, *Grass on the Wayside* is Sōseki's only autobiographical novel and the first book of its kind to appear in modern Japan. It is the story of Kenzo, Sōseki's alter ego, an unhappy, self-centered man. The book is remarkable not only for the depth and liveliness of its supporting characters—no modern Japanese novelist ever created as complex a personality as Kenzo's wife—but also for its treatment of Kenzo himself, who remains one of the most fully developed characters in Japanese fiction.

The Three-Cornered World

Translated by Alan Turney

ISBN 4-8053-0201-1

In *The Three-Cornered World*, an artist leaves city life to wander in the mountains on a quest to stimulate his artistic endeavors. When he finds himself staying at an almost deserted inn, he becomes obsessed with the beautiful and strange daughter of the innkeeper, who is rumored to have abandoned her husband and fallen in love with a priest at a nearby temple. Haunted by her aura of mystery and tragedy, he decides to paint her. As he struggles to complete his picture, his daily conversations with those at the inn in the village provide clues and inspiration towards solving the enigma of her life.

Mon

Translated by Francis Mathy

ISBN 4-8053-0291-7

Mon is an intimate story of the consequences of an impulsive marriage, keenly portrayed in the daily life of a young couple and the quiet frustration, isolation and helplessness they face. Alienated from friends and relatives, living a lonely and frugal life, the wife, Oyone, placidly accepts their fate and blames herself for her ill health and their inability to have children. Sosuke, the husband, is content with their lives as they are. Things change when Koroku, Sosuke's much younger brother, comes to live with them. Not only does he become Sosuke's responsibility, but he also provides the impetus for Sosuke to finally re-examine his place in the world.

Kokoro

Translated by Edwin McClellan

ISBN 4-8053-0161-9

Written in 1914, *Kokoro* provides a timeless psychological analysis of a man's alienation from society. It tells the story of a solitary and intensely torn scholar during the Meiji era. A chance encounter on the beaches of Kamakura irrevocably links a young student to a man he simply calls "Sensei". The student gradually learns the reasons for Sensei's aloofness and withdrawal from the world, and finally the tale of guilt in his marriage and what he believes to be his betrayal of a friend.